The Human Body in Health & Disease
for Ross Medical Education Center

Fifth Edition

Linda Swisher, RN, EdD

MOSBY

ELSEVIER

MOSBY
ELSEVIER

3251 Riverport Ln.
Maryland Heights, MO 63043

Study Guide to Accompany The Human Body in Health & Disease   ISBN: 978-0-323-08653-0
for Ross Medical Education Center, Fifth Edition

Notice

Neither the Publisher nor the Authors assume any responsibility for any loss or injury and/or damage to persons or property arising out of or related to any use of the material contained in this book. It is the responsibility of the treating practitioner, relying on independent expertise and knowledge of the patient, to determine the best treatment and method of application for the patient.

The Publisher

International Standard Book Number: 978-0-323-08653-0

Acquisitions Editor: Scott Weaver
Developmental Editor: Yejoon Koh
Publishing Services Manager: Pat Joiner-Myers
Project Manager: Stephen Bancroft

Printed in the United States of America
Last digit is the print number: 9 8 7 6 5 4 3 2 1

Acknowledgments

I wish to express my appreciation to the staff of Mosby, Inc., especially Tom Wilhelm, Jeff Downing, Karen Turner, and Jennifer Shropshire for opening the door and assisting me with this text. My continued admiration and gratitude to Kevin Patton and Gary Thibodeau for an outstanding text. Your time and dedication to science education will, I hope, inspire potential caregivers and improve the quality of health care for the future.

To my family and Brian, my thanks for your assistance and support.

To Bill, who is always there, my thanks for the whispers of inspiration.

Finally, to the designer of the human body, this book is dedicated. What a miraculous creation!

Linda Swisher, RN, EdD

Preface

TO THE INSTRUCTOR

This Study Guide is designed to help your students master basic anatomy and physiology. It works in two ways.

First, the section of the preface titled "To the Student," contains detailed instructions on:

- How to achieve good grades in anatomy and physiology
- How to read the textbook
- How to use the exercises in this Study Guide
- How to use visual memory as a learning tool
- How to use mnemonic devices as learning aids
- How to prepare for an examination
- How to take an examination
- How to find out why questions were missed on an examination

Second, the Study Guide itself contains features that facilitate learning:

1. LEARNING OBJECTIVES, designed to break down the process of learning into small units. The questions in this Study Guide have been developed to help the student master the learning objectives identified at the beginning of each chapter in the text. The Guide is also sequenced to correspond to key areas of each chapter. A variety of questions have been prepared to cover the material effectively and expose the student to multiple learning approaches.

2. CROSSWORD PUZZLES, to encourage the use of new vocabulary words and emphasize the proper spelling of these terms.

3. OPTIONAL APPLICATION QUESTIONS, particularly targeted for the health occupations student, but appropriate for any student of anatomy and physiology because questions are based entirely on information contained within the chapter.

4. DIAGRAMS with key features marked by numbers for identification. Students can easily check their work by comparing the diagram in the workbook with the equivalent figure in the text.

These features should make mastery of the material a rewarding experience for both instructor and student.

TO THE STUDENT

How to Achieve Good Grades in Anatomy and Physiology

This Study Guide is designed to help you be successful in learning anatomy and physiology. Before you begin using the Study Guide, read the following suggestions. Successful students understand effective study techniques and have good study habits.

How to Read the Textbook

Keep up with the reading assignments. Read the textbook assignment before the instructor covers the material in a lecture. If you have failed to read the assignment beforehand, you may not grasp what the instructor is talking about in the lecture. When you read, do the following:

1. As you finish reading a sentence, ask yourself if you understand it. If you do not, put a question mark in the margin by that sentence. If the instructor does not clarify the material in lecture, ask him or her to explain it to you further.

2. Do the learning objectives in the text. A learning objective is a specific task that you are expected to be able to do after you have read a chapter. It sets specific goals for the student and breaks down learning into small units. It emphasizes the key points that the author is making in the chapter.

3. Underline and make notes in the margin to highlight key ideas, mark something you need to reinforce at a later time, or indicate things that you do not understand.

4. If you come to a word you do not understand, look it up in a dictionary. Write the word on one side of an index card and its definition on the other side. Carry these cards with you, and when you have a spare minute, use them like flash cards. If you do not know how to spell or pronounce a word, you will have a hard time remembering it.

5. Carefully study each diagram and illustration as you read. Many students ignore these aids. The author included them to help students understand the material.

6. Summarize what you read. After finishing a paragraph, try to restate the main ideas. Do this again when you finish the chapter. Identify and mentally restate the main concepts of the chapter. Check to see if you are correct. In short, be an active reader. Do not just stare at a page or read it superficially.

7. Finally, attack each unit of learning with a positive mental attitude. Motivation and perseverance are prime factors in achieving good grades. The combination of your instructor, the text, the Study Guide, and your dedicated work will lead to success in anatomy and physiology.

How to Use the Exercises in this Study Guide

After you have read a chapter and learned all of the new words, begin working with the Study Guide. Read the overview of the chapter, which summarizes the main points.

Familiarize yourself with the "Topics for Review" section, which emphasizes the learning objectives outlined in the text. Complete the questions and diagrams in the Study Guide. Questions are grouped into specific topics that correspond to the text. Each major topic of the Study and Review Guide provides references to specific areas of the text, so if you are having difficulty with a particular grouping of questions you have a specific reference area to assist you with remedial work. This feature allows you to identify your area of weakness accurately. A variety of questions are offered throughout the Study Guide to help you cover the material effectively. The following examples are among the exercises that have been included to assist you.

Multiple Choice Questions

Multiple choice questions will have only one correct answer for you to select from the several possibilities presented. There are two types of multiple choice questions that you need to be acquainted with:

1. "None of the above is correct" questions. These questions test your ability to recall rather than recognize the correct answer. You would select the "none of the above" choice only if all the other choices in that particular question were incorrect.

2. Sequence questions. These questions test your ability to arrange a list of structures in the correct order. In this type of question, you are asked to determine the sequence of the structures given in the various choices, and then you are to select the structure listed that would be third in that sequence, as in this example.

Which one of the following structures is the third through which food passes?
A. Stomach
B. Mouth
C. Large intestine
D. Esophagus
E. Anus

The correct answer is *A*.

Matching Questions

Matching questions ask the student to select the correct answer from a list of terms and to write that answer in the space provided.

True or False Questions

True or false questions ask you to write "T" in the answer space if you agree with that statement. If you disagree with the statement, you will circle the incorrect word(s) and write the correct word(s) in the answer space.

Identify the Term that Does Not Belong

In questions that ask you to identify the incorrect term, three words are given that relate to each other in structure or function, and one more word is included that has no relationship, or has an opposing relationship to the other three terms. You are asked to circle the term that does not relate to the others. An example might be: iris, cornea, stapes, retina. You would circle the word *stapes* because all other terms refer to the eye.

Fill-in-the-Blank Questions

Fill-in-the-blank questions ask you to recall one or more missing words and insert them into the answer blanks. These questions may involve sentences or paragraphs.

Application Questions

Application questions ask you to make judgments about a situation based on the information in the chapter. These questions may concern how you would respond to a situation or ask you to suggest a possible diagnosis for a set of symptoms.

Charts

Several charts have been included that correspond to figures in the text. Areas have been omitted so that you can fill them in and test your recall of these important concepts.

Word Find Puzzles

The Study Guide includes word find puzzles that allow you to identify key terms in the chapter in an interesting and challenging way.

Crossword Puzzles

Vocabulary words from the "New Words" section at the end of each chapter of the text have been developed into crossword puzzles. This encourages recall and proper spelling. Occasionally, an exercise uses scrambled words to encourage recall and spelling.

Labeling Exercises

Labeling exercises present diagrams with parts that are not identified. For each of these diagrams, you are to print the name of each numbered part on the appropriately numbered line. You may choose to further distinguish the structures by coloring them with a variety of colors.

Check Your Knowledge

This section selects questions from throughout the chapter to provide you with a final review. This mini-test gives you an overview of your knowledge of the entire chapter after completing all of the other sections. It emphasizes the main concepts of the unit, but should not be attempted until the specific topics of the chapter have been mastered.

How to Use Visual Memory

Visual memory is another important tool in learning. If I asked you to picture an elephant in your mind, with all its external parts labeled, you could do that easily. Visual memory is a powerful key to learning. Whenever possible, try to build a memory picture. Remember: a picture is worth a thousand words.

Visual memory works especially well with the sequencing of items, such as circulatory pathways and the passage of air or food. Students who try to learn sequencing by memorizing a list of words do poorly on examinations. If they forget one word in the sequence, they then may forget the remaining words as well. With a memory picture you can pick out the important features.

How to Use Mnemonic Devices

Mnemonic devices are little jingles that you memorize to help you remember things. If you make up your own, they will stick with you longer. Here are three examples of such devices:

"On Old Olympus' towering tops a Finn and German viewed some hops." This one is used to remember the cranial nerves. Each word begins with the same letter as does the name of one of the nerves: olfactory, optic, oculomotor, trochlear, trigeminal, abducens, facial, auditory, glossopharyngeal, vagus, sensory (accessory), and hypoglossal.

"C. Hopkins CaFe where they serve Mg NaCl." This mnemonic device reminds you of the chemical symbols for the biologically important electrolytes: carbon, hydrogen, oxygen, phosphorus, potassium, iodine, nitrogen, sulfur, calcium, iron, magnesium, sodium, chlorine.

"Roy G. Biv." This mnemonic device helps you remember the colors of the visible light spectrum: red, orange, yellow, green, blue, indigo, violet.

How to Prepare for an Examination

Prepare far in advance for an examination. Actually, your preparation for an examination should begin on the first day of class. Keeping up with your assignments daily makes the final preparation for an examination much easier. You should begin your final preparation at least three nights before the test. Last-minute studying usually means poor results and limited retention.

1. Make sure that you understand and can answer all of the learning objectives for the chapter on which you are being tested.

2. Review the appropriate questions in this Study Guide. Review is something that you should do after every class and at the end of every study session. It is important to keep going over the material until you have a thorough understanding of the chapter and rapid recall of its contents. If review becomes a daily habit, studying for the actual examination will not be difficult. Go through each question and write down an answer. Do the same with the labeling of each structure on the appropriate diagrams. If you have already done this as part of your daily review, cover the answers with a piece of paper and quiz yourself again.

3. As you read a chapter, ask yourself what questions you would ask if you were writing a test on that unit. You will most likely ask yourself many of the questions that will show up on your examinations.

4. Get a good night's sleep before the test. Staying up late and upsetting your biorhythms will only make you less efficient during the test.

How to Take an Examination

The Day of the Test

1. Get up early enough to avoid rushing. Eat appropriately. Your body needs fuel, but a heavy meal just before a test is not a good idea.

2. Keep calm. Briefly look over your notes. If you have prepared for the test properly, there will be no need for last-minute cramming.

3. Make certain that you have everything you need for the test: pens, pencils, test sheets, and so forth.

4. Allow enough time to get to the examination site. Missing your bus, getting stuck in traffic, or being unable to find a parking space will not put you in a good frame of mind to do well on the examination.

During the Examination

1. Pay careful attention to the instructions for the test.

2. Note any corrections.

3. Budget your time so that you will be able to finish the test.

4. Ask the instructor for clarification if you do not understand a question or an instruction.

5. Concentrate on your own test paper and do not allow yourself to be distracted by others in the room.

Hints for Taking a Multiple-Choice Test

1. Read each question carefully. Pay attention to each word.

2. Cross out obviously wrong choices and think about those that are left.

3. Go through the test once, quickly answering the questions you are sure of; then go back over the test and answer the rest of the questions.

4. Fill in the answer spaces completely and make your marks heavy. Erase answers completely if you make a mistake.

5. If you must guess, stick with your first hunch. Most often, students will change right answers to wrong ones.

6. If you will not be penalized for guessing, do not leave any blanks.

Hints for Taking an Essay Test

1. Budget time for each question.

2. Write legibly and try to spell words correctly.

3. Be concise, complete, and specific. Do not be repetitious or long-winded.

4. Organize your answer in an outline—this helps not only you but also the person who grades the test.

5. Answer each question as thoroughly as you can, but leave some room for possible additions.

Hints for Taking a Laboratory Practical Examination

Students often have a hard time with this kind of test. Visual memory is very important here. To put it simply, you must be able to identify every structure you have studied. If you are unable to identify a structure, then you will be unable to answer any questions about that structure.

Possible questions that could appear on an examination of this type might include:

1. Identification of a structure, organ, or feature.

2. Identification of the function of a structure, organ, or feature.

3. Sequence questions for air flow, passage of food or urine, and so forth.

4. Disease questions (for example, if an organ fails, what disease will result?).

How to Find Out Why Questions Were Missed on an Examination

After the Examination

Go over your test after it has been scored to see what you missed and why you missed it. You can pick up important clues that will help you on future examinations. Ask yourself these questions:

1. Did I miss questions because I did not read them carefully?

2. Did I miss questions because I had gaps in my knowledge?

3. Did I miss questions because I could not determine scientific words?

4. Did I miss questions because I did not have good visual memory of things?

Be sure to go back and learn the things you did not know. Chances are these topics will come up on the final examination.

Your grades in other classes will improve as well when you apply these study methods. Learning should be fun. With these helpful hints and this Study Guide you should be able to achieve the grades you desire. Good luck!

Contents

Chapter 1	An Introduction to the Structure and Function of the Body	1
Chapter 2	Chemistry of Life	11
Chapter 3	Cells and Tissues	19
Chapter 4	Organ Systems of the Body	31
Chapter 5	Mechanisms of Disease	39
Chapter 6	The Integumentary System and Body Membranes	51
Chapter 7	The Skeletal System	63
Chapter 8	The Muscular System	79
Chapter 9	The Nervous System	91
Chapter 10	The Senses	111
Chapter 11	The Endocrine System	123
Chapter 12	Blood	135
Chapter 13	The Heart and Heart Disease	145
Chapter 14	The Circulation of the Blood	155
Chapter 15	The Lymphatic System and Immunity	167
Chapter 16	The Respiratory System	177
Chapter 17	The Digestive System	189
Chapter 18	Nutrition and Metabolism	209
Chapter 19	The Urinary System	217
Chapter 20	Fluid and Electrolyte Balance	229
Chapter 21	Acid-Base Balance	237
Chapter 22	The Reproductive Systems	245
Chapter 23	Growth and Development	263
Chapter 24	Genetics and Genetic Diseases	273

CHAPTER 2

Chemistry of Life

Although anatomy can be studied without knowledge of the principles of chemistry, it is hard to imagine having an understanding of physiology without a basic comprehension of chemical reactions in the body. Trillions of cells make up the various levels of organization in the body. Our health and survival depends upon the proper chemical maintenance in the cytoplasm of our cells.

Chemists use the terms *elements* or *compounds* to describe all of the substances (matter) in and around us. What distinguishes these two terms is their basic structure. An element cannot be broken down. A compound, on the other hand, is made up of two or more elements and can be broken down into the elements that form it.

Organic and inorganic compounds are equally important to our survival. Without organic compounds, such as carbohydrates, proteins, and fats, and inorganic compounds, such as water, we could not sustain life.

Because we cannot see many of the chemical reactions that take place daily in our bodies, it is sometimes difficult to comprehend the principles involved in initiating them. Chemicals are responsible for directing virtually all of our bodily functions. Therefore, it is important to master the fundamental concepts of chemistry in order to understand physiology.

TOPICS FOR REVIEW

Before progressing to Chapter 3, you should have an understanding of the basic chemical reactions in the body and the fundamental concepts of biochemistry.

LEVELS OF CHEMICAL ORGANIZATION

Multiple Choice

Circle the correct answer.

1. Which of the following is *not* a subatomic particle?
   A. Proton
   B. Electron
   C. Isotope
   D. Neutron

2. Electrons move about within certain limits called:
   A. Energy levels
   B. Orbitals
   C. Chemical bonding
   D. Shells

3. The number of protons in the nucleus is an atom's:
   A. Atomic mass
   B. Atomic energy level
   C. Atomic number
   D. None of the above

4. The number of protons and neutrons combined is the atom's:
   A. Atomic mass
   B. Atomic energy level
   C. Orbit
   D. Chemical bonding

5. Which of the following is *not* one of the major elements present in the human body?
   A. Oxygen
   B. Carbon
   C. Nitrogen
   D. Iron

6. Atoms usually unite with each other to form larger chemical units called:
   A. Energy levels
   B. Mass
   C. Molecules
   D. Shells

7. Substances whose molecules have more than one element in them are called:
   A. Compounds
   B. Orbitals
   C. Elements
   D. Neutrons

True or False

For each of the following statements, write "T" in the answer blank if it is true. If the statement is false, circle the incorrect word(s) and write the correct word(s) in the answer blank.

_____ 8. *Matter* is anything that occupies space and has mass.

_____ 9. In the body, most chemicals are in the form of electrons.

_____ 10. At the core of each atom is a nucleus composed of positively charged protons and negatively charged neutrons.

_____ 11. Orbitals are arranged into *energy levels* depending on their distance from the nucleus.

_____ 12. The *formula* for a compound contains symbols that represent each element in the molecule.

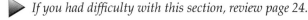 *If you had difficulty with this section, review page 24.*

CHEMICAL BONDING

Multiple Choice

Circle the correct answer.

13. Ionic bonds are chemical bonds formed by the:
    A. Sharing of electrons between atoms
    B. Donation of protons from one atom to another
    C. Donation of electrons from one atom to another
    D. Acceptance of protons from one atom to another

14. Molecules that form ions when dissolved in water are called:
    A. Covalent bonds
    B. Electrolytes
    C. Isotopes
    D. Ionic bonds

15. When atoms share electrons, a/an _____ forms.
    A. Covalent bond
    B. Electrolyte
    C. Ionic bond
    D. Isotope

16. Covalent bonds:
    A. Break apart easily in water
    B. Are not easily broken
    C. Donate electrons
    D. None of the above

17. An example of an ionic bond is:
    A. NaCl
    B. Ca
    C. O
    D. P

18. If a molecule "dissociates" in water, it:
    A. Has taken on additional ions
    B. Has eliminated ions
    C. Separates to form free ions
    D. Forms a covalent bond

▷ *If you had difficulty with this section, review pages 25-27.*

INORGANIC CHEMISTRY

Match each term with its corresponding description or definition.

_____ 19. A type of compound

_____ 20. Compound essential to life

_____ 21. Dissolves solutes

_____ 22. Water plus common salt

_____ 23. Reactants combine only after (H) and (O) atoms are removed

_____ 24. Combine to form a larger product

_____ 25. The reverse of dehydration synthesis

_____ 26. Yields energy for muscle contraction

_____ 27. Alkaline compound

_____ 28. A measure of the H+ concentration

_____ 29. Easily dissociates to form H+ ions

_____ 30. Dissociates very little

A. Aqueous solution
B. Water
C. ATP
D. Base
E. Solvent
F. pH
G. Dehydration synthesis
H. Inorganic
I. Weak acid
J. Hydrolysis
K. Strong acid
L. Reactants

▷ *If you had difficulty with this section, review pages 27-30.*

ORGANIC CHEMISTRY

Match each numbered term with its category. Write the corresponding letter in the blank.

A. Carbohydrate   B. Lipid   C. Protein   D. Nucleic acid

_____ 31. Monosaccharide

_____ 32. Triglyceride

_____ 33. DNA

_____ 34. Cholesterol

_____ 35. Amino acid

_____ 36. Glycogen

_____ 37. Sucrose

_____ 38. Phospholipid

_____ 39. Contains C, O, H, and N

_____ 40. RNA

▶ *If you had difficulty with this section, review pages 30-35.*

UNSCRAMBLE THE WORDS

41. **N T E I P O R**

```
[ ][ ][O][ ][ ][ ]
```

42. **S E B A**

```
[ ][ ][O][ ]
```

43. **K L A L A N I E**

```
[ ][ ][ ][O][ ][ ][ ][ ]
```

44. **D L P I I**

```
[O][ ][ ][ ][ ]
```

Take the circled letters, unscramble them, and fill in the solution.

What was missing from the Thanksgiving dinner?

45.
```
[ ][ ][ ][ ][ ]
```

Fill in the crossword puzzle.

Across
1. Below 7.0 on pH scale
2. Bond formed by sharing electrons
5. Occupies space and has mass
6. Reverse of dehydration synthesis
7. Substances composed of one type of atom
8. Uncharged subatomic particle
9. Subatomic particle

Down
1. Combine to form molecules
2. Substances whose molecules have more than one element
3. Amino acid
4. Polysaccharide
7. Chemical catalyst
10. Fat

APPLYING WHAT YOU KNOW

46. Kim just finished preparing a meal of pan-fried hamburgers for her family. While the frying pan was still hot, she poured the liquid grease into a metal container to cool. Later, she noticed that the liquid oil had solidified as it cooled. Explain the chemistry of why the then room-temperature fat was solid.

47. Carol was gaining weight, yet she was eating very little. Her physician suspected hypothyroidism and suggested a test that measures radiation emitted by the thyroid when radioactive iodine is introduced into the gland. Describe what the radiologist will do to evaluate Carol's thyroid function.

48. Word Find

Find and circle 12 terms presented in this chapter. Words may be spelled top to bottom, bottom to top, right to left, left to right, or diagonally.

Alkaline
Atomic mass
Base
Carbohydrate
Dehydration
Dissociation

Electrolyte
Molecule
Nucleic acid
Proton
Reactant
Solvent

```
E T A R D Y H O B R A C E
T B H S I H L I N A T O D
B N E H S G O U L P O T E
R Z A M S F R K U S M T H
P R O T O N A I E C I X Y
B R N U C L E I C A C I D
C A F T I A E W G G M W R
L E S N A B E C E E A E A
G Q E E T E A R U S S F T
Q R P V I B Y K I L S W I
E T Y L O R T C E L E B O
S B U O N E S P N B R B N
O P J S T D J M O L U H D
```

DID YOU KNOW?

After a vigorous workout, your triglycerides fall 10% to 20% and your HDL increases by the same percentage for 2 to 3 hours.

CHECK YOUR KNOWLEDGE

Fill in the blanks.

1. _____ is the field of science devoted to studying the chemical aspects of life.

2. Atoms are composed of protons, electrons, and _____.

3. The farther an orbital extends from the nucleus, the _____ its energy level.

4. Substances can be classified as _____ or _____.

5. Chemical bonds form to make atoms more _____.

6. A(n) _____ is an electrically charged atom.

7. Few _____ compounds have carbon atoms in them and none have C-C or C-H bonds.

8. _____ is a reaction in which water is lost from the reactants.

9. Chemists often use a _____ to represent a chemical reaction.

10. High levels of _____ in the blood make the blood more acidic.

11. _____ are compounds that produce an excess of H+ ions.

12. _____ maintain pH balance by preventing sudden changes in the H+ ion concentration.

13. _____ literally means "carbon" and "water."

14. _____ is a steroid lipid.

15. Collagen and keratin are examples of _____ proteins.

16. A _____ _____ _____ is formed when the twists and folds of the secondary structure fold again to form a three-dimensional structure.

17. A _____ _____ _____ is a sequence of amino acids in a chain.

18. In the DNA molecule, nucleotides are arranged in a twisted strand called a _____ _____.

19. RNA uses the same set of bases as DNA except for the substitution of _____ for thymine.

20. Glycogen and starch are examples of _____.

CHAPTER 4

Organ Systems of the Body

A smooth-running automobile is the result of many systems working together harmoniously. The engine, the fuel system, the exhaust system, the brake system, and the cooling system are but a few of the many complex structural units that the automobile as a whole relies on to keep it functioning smoothly. So it is with the human body. We, too, depend on the successful performance of many individual systems working together to create and maintain a healthy human being.

When you have completed your review of the 11 major organ systems and the organs that make up these systems, you will find your understanding of the performance of the body as a whole much more meaningful.

TOPICS FOR REVIEW

Before progressing to Chapter 5, you should have an understanding of the 11 major organ systems and be able to identify the organs that are included in each system. Your review should also include current approaches to organ replacement.

ORGAN SYSTEMS OF THE BODY

Match each term on the left with its corresponding term on the right.

Group A

_____	1. Integumentary	A.	Hair
_____	2. Skeletal	B.	Spinal cord
_____	3. Muscular	C.	Hormones
_____	4. Nervous	D.	Tendons
_____	5. Endocrine	E.	Joints

Group B

_____	6. Cardiovascular	A.	Esophagus
_____	7. Lymphatic	B.	Ureters
_____	8. Urinary	C.	Larynx
_____	9. Digestive	D.	Genitalia
_____	10. Respiratory	E.	Spleen
_____	11. Reproductive	F.	Capillaries

Circle the word in each word group that does not belong.

12. Pharynx	Trachea	Mouth	Alveoli
13. Uterus	Rectum	Gonads	Prostate
14. Veins	Arteries	Heart	Pancreas
15. Pineal	Bladder	Ureters	Urethra
16. Tendon	Smooth	Joints	Voluntary
17. Pituitary	Brain	Spinal cord	Nerves
18. Cartilage	Joints	Ligaments	Tendons
19. Hormones	Pituitary	Pancreas	Appendix
20. Thymus	Nails	Hair	Oil glands
21. Esophagus	Pharynx	Mouth	Trachea
22. Thymus	Spleen	Tonsils	Liver

23. Fill in the missing areas.

SYSTEM	ORGANS	FUNCTIONS
1. Integumentary	Skin, nails, hair, sense receptors, sweat glands, oil glands	
2. Skeletal		Support, movement, storage of minerals, blood formation
3. Muscular	Muscles	
4.	Brain, spinal cord, nerves	Communication, integration, control, recognition of sensory stimuli
5. Endocrine		Secretion of hormones; communication, integration, control
6. Cardiovascular	Heart, blood vessels	
7. Lymphatic		Transportation, immune system
8.	Kidneys, ureters, bladder, urethra	Elimination of wastes, electrolyte balance, acid-base balance, water balance
9. Digestive		Digestion of food, absorption of nutrients
10.	Nose, pharynx, larynx, trachea, bronchi, lungs	Exchange of gases in the lungs
11. Reproductive		Survival of species; production of sex cells, fertilization, development, birth; nourishment of offspring; production of hormones

▶ *If you had difficulty with this section, review pages 79-93 and the chapter summary on pages 97-99.*

ORGAN TRANSPLANTATION

Fill in the blanks.

24. An organ not required for life to continue is a _____
_____.

25. Many people suffering from deafness have had their hearing partially restored by "artificial ears" called _____ _____.

26. One of the earliest devices to augment vital functions was the "artificial kidney" or _____ _____.

27. Electromechanical devices that help keep blood pumping in patients suffering from end-stage heart disease are known as _____ _____ _____ _____.

28. One approach that offers the hope of a permanent solution to loss of vital organ function is _____ _____.

29. After cancerous breasts are removed, "new" breasts can be formed from skin and muscle tissue using a method known as _____ _____ _____.

30. The advantage to using a patient's own tissues in organ replacement is that the possibility of _____ is reduced.

▶ *If you had difficulty with this section, review pages 93-97.*

UNSCRAMBLE THE WORDS

31. **R T A H E**

32. **I E P L N A**

33. **E E N V R**

34. **S U H E S O P G A**

Take the circled letters, unscramble them, and fill in the statement.

you have exactly ten minutes...

The more thoroughly you review this chapter, the less

35. ☐☐☐☐☐☐☐ **you will be during your test.**

APPLYING WHAT YOU KNOW

36. Myrna was 15 years old and had not yet started menstruating. Her family physician decided to consult two other physicians, each of whom specialized in a different system. Specialists in the areas of _____ and _____ were consulted.

37. Brian was admitted to the hospital with second- and third-degree burns over 50% of his body. He was placed in isolation. When Jenny went to visit him, she was required to wear a hospital gown and mask. Why was Brian placed in isolation? Why was Jenny required to wear special attire?

38. Sheila had a mastectomy to remove a cancerous lesion in her breast. Her body rejected the breast implant used to reconstruct her breast. Is there another breast reconstruction option that can be offered to Sheila? If so, explain this option.

39. Word Find

Find and circle the names of 11 organ systems. Words may be spelled top to bottom, bottom to top, right to left, left to right, or diagonally.

```
Y R A T N E M U G E T N I R F
H N E R V O U S K I R J M G T
L Y M P H A T I C I S Y Y U I
B N X Y R O T A L U C R I C W
P E L R E O M J M S O M M P S
C C W M A N D L A T E L E K S
R R K E M L I U A A V V U K N
D K X P D J U R C J I R Q E M
C D B V C V I C C T T K W C X
X R Q Q D P H C S O I X P A Z
M F M U S Y D E V U D V Y K E
U E S E C Z G T Q D M N E K O
P Y R A N I R U C T C N E W H
N H T N D E P S I X A Q O I E
```

Circulatory	Lymphatic	Respiratory
Digestive	Muscular	Skeletal
Endocrine	Nervous	Urinary
Integumentary	Reproductive	

DID YOU KNOW?

Muscles comprise 40% of your body weight. Your skeleton, however, only accounts for 18% of your body weight.

ORGAN SYSTEMS

Fill in the crossword puzzle.

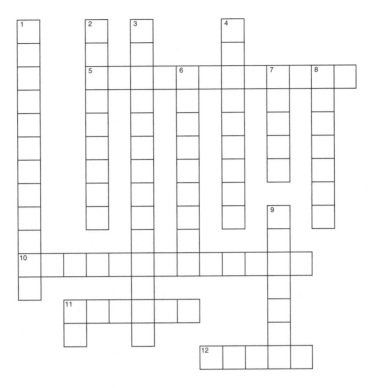

ACROSS

5. Specialized signal of nervous system (two words)
10. Skin
11. Testes and ovaries
12. Undigested residue of digestion

DOWN

1. Inflammation of the appendix
2. Vulva, penis, and scrotum
3. Heart and blood vessels
4. Subdivision of circulatory system
6. System of hormones
7. Waste product of kidneys
8. Agent that causes change in the activity of a structure
9. Chemical secretion of endocrine system
11. Gastrointestinal tract (abbreviation)

CHECK YOUR KNOWLEDGE

Multiple Choice

Circle the correct answer.

1. Which body system serves to clean the blood of waste products?
    A. Digestive
    B. Endocrine
    C. Cardiovascular
    D. Urinary

2. Ovaries and testes are considered components of which system?
    A. Reproductive system
    B. Endocrine system
    C. Both A and B
    D. None of the above

3. Which of the following organs is classified as an accessory organ of the digestive system?
    A. Mouth
    B. Esophagus
    C. Tongue
    D. Anal canal

4. Factors in the environment such as heat, light, pressure, and temperature that can be recognized by the nervous system are called:
    A. Effectors
    B. Stimuli
    C. Receptors
    D. Nerve impulses

5. Which body system stores the mineral calcium?
    A. Cardiovascular
    B. Digestive
    C. Lymphatic
    D. Skeletal

6. What is undigested material in the gastrointestinal tract called?
    A. Feces
    B. Urine
    C. Lymph
    D. Blood

7. Which body system produces heat and maintains body posture?
    A. Endocrine
    B. Muscular
    C. Cardiovascular
    D. Skeletal

8. Which of the following is *not* a function of the integumentary system?
    A. Integration
    B. Temperature regulation
    C. Ability to serve as a sense organ
    D. Protection

9. Which of the following is *not* a component of the digestive system?
    A. Spleen
    B. Liver
    C. Pancreas
    D. Gallbladder

10. When a group of tissues starts working together to perform a common function, what level of organization is achieved?
    A. Systemic
    B. Tissue
    C. Organ
    D. Cellular

Matching

Match each word in column A with the most appropriate corresponding word in column B. (There is only one correct answer for each.)

Column A

_____ 11. Sweat glands

_____ 12. Heart

_____ 13. Spleen

_____ 14. Vas deferens

_____ 15. Bladder

_____ 16. Gallbladder

_____ 17. Uterine tubes

_____ 18. Trachea

_____ 19. Spinal cord

_____ 20. Adrenals

Column B

A. Endocrine

B. Urinary

C. Integumentary

D. Cardiovascular

E. Respiratory

F. Digestive

G. Male reproductive

H. Lymphatic

I. Female reproductive

J. Nervous

MECHANISMS OF DISEASE

Fill in the crossword puzzle.

ACROSS

1. Roundworm
3. "Cancer gene"
5. Rod-shaped cells
6. Round cells
7. Spreads disease to other organisms
9. Lack chlorophyll
10. Possess pseudopodia
11. Tissue swelling

DOWN

2. Glandular cancer
4. Microscopic organism
8. Thick inflammatory exudate

CHECK YOUR KNOWLEDGE

Multiple Choice

Circle the correct answer.

1. Diseases with undetermined causes are:
   A. Asymptomatic
   B. Idiopathic
   C. Psychogenic
   D. Predisposing

2. The study of the occurrence, distribution, and transmission of diseases is:
   A. Entomology
   B. Pathology
   C. Oncology
   D. Epidemiology

3. Streptomycin is an example of a/an:
   A. Antibiotic
   B. Vaccine
   C. Pathogenic organism
   D. All of the above

4. Reversal of a chronic condition is called:
   A. Inflammatory response
   B. Predisposing condition
   C. Hemostasis
   D. Remission

5. If antibodies are found in an immunological test, it is assumed that:
   A. The patient has been exposed to a pathogen
   B. The infection is gone
   C. A and B
   D. None of the above

6. An epidemiologist:
   A. Studies the transmission of disease
   B. Monitors infection control programs
   C. Tracks the spread of disease
   D. All of the above

7. Study of the underlying physiological processes associated with disease leads to:
   A. Strategies of prevention
   B. Strategies of treatment
   C. A and B
   D. None of the above

8. Severe loss of appetite, weight loss, and general weakness in a cancer patient describe:
   A. Secondary infection
   B. Cachexia
   C. Inflammatory response
   D. Chemotaxis

9. Intracellular parasites that are not technically living organisms are characteristics of:
   A. Bacteria
   B. Fungi
   C. Amoebas
   D. Viruses

10. Examples of protozoa include all of the following *except*:
    A. Bacilli
    B. Flagellates
    C. Sporozoa
    D. Amoebas

Matching

Match each term in column A with the most appropriate definition or description in column B. (Only one answer is correct for each.)

Column A

_____ 11. Syndrome

_____ 12. Metastasis

_____ 13. Anaerobic

_____ 14. Protozoa

_____ 15. Pathogenesis

_____ 16. Fever

_____ 17. Metazoa

_____ 18. Pathology

_____ 19. Neoplasm

_____ 20. Arthropods

Column B

A. Study of disease

B. Require absence of oxygen

C. Collection of signs and symptoms

D. Spread of cancer cells

E. Multicellular organisms that parasitize humans

F. Abnormal cell growth

G. Pattern of disease development

H. Mites

I. Inflammatory response

J. One-celled organisms that parasitize cells

MAJOR GROUPS OF PATHOGENIC BACTERIA

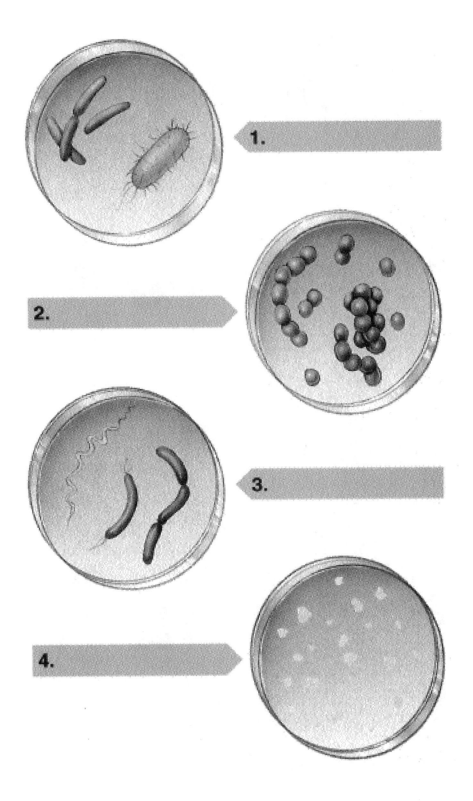

MAJOR GROUPS OF PATHOGENIC PROTOZOA

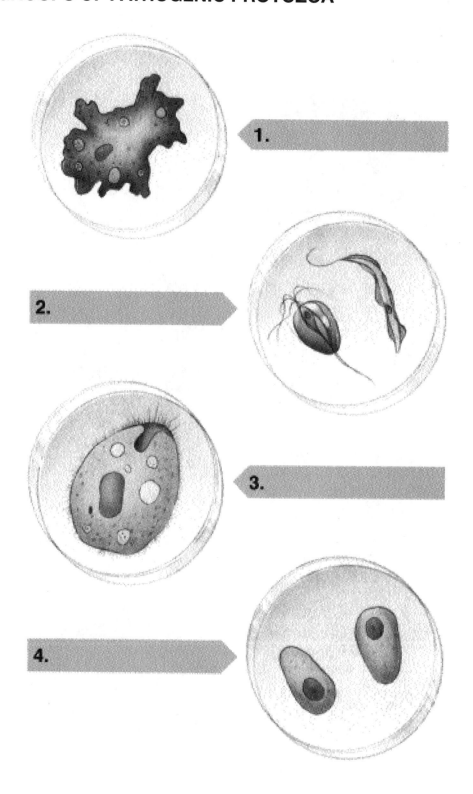

EXAMPLES OF PATHOGENIC ANIMALS

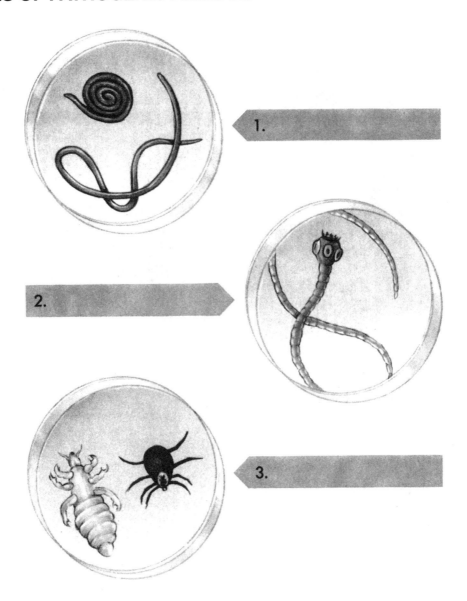

MAJOR GROUPS OF PATHOGENIC FUNGI

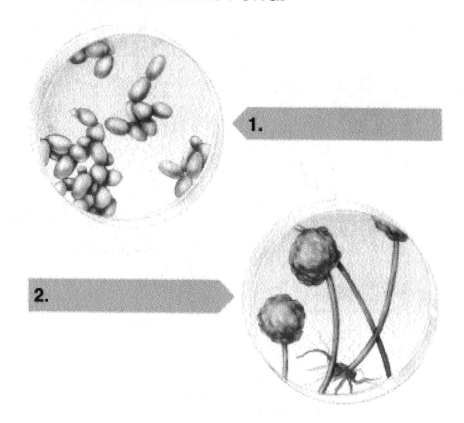

Matching

Match each term in column A with its corresponding description in column B. (Only one answer is correct for each.)

Column A

_____ 11. Diarthroses

_____ 12. Spongy bone

_____ 13. Synarthrosis

_____ 14. Foramen magnum

_____ 15. Calcaneus

_____ 16. Chondrocyte

_____ 17. Compact bone

_____ 18. Ethmoid

_____ 19. Coxal

_____ 20. Hematopoiesis

Column B

A. Haversian canal

B. Trabeculae

C. Perpendicular plate

D. Red bone marrow

E. Tarsal

F. Ilium

G. Synovial fluid

H. Cartilage

I. Suture

J. Occipital bone

LONGITUDINAL SECTION OF LONG BONE

1. _____

2. _____

3. _____

4. _____

5. _____

6. _____

7. _____

8. _____

9. _____

10. _____

11. _____

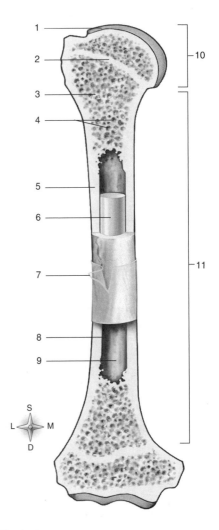

ANTERIOR VIEW OF SKELETON

1. _____

2. _____

3. _____

4. _____

5. _____

6. _____

7. _____

8. _____

9. _____

10. _____

11. _____

12. _____

13. _____

14. _____

15. _____

16. _____

17. _____

18. _____

19. _____

20. _____

21. _____

22. _____

23. _____

24. _____

25. _____

26. _____

27. _____

28. _____

29. _____

30. _____

POSTERIOR VIEW OF SKELETON

1. _____

2. _____

3. _____

4. _____

5. _____

6. _____

7. _____

8. _____

9. _____

10. _____

11. _____

12. _____

13. _____

14. _____

15. _____

16. _____

17. _____

18. _____

19. _____

20. _____

21. _____

22. _____

23. _____

24. _____

25. _____

26. _____

27. _____

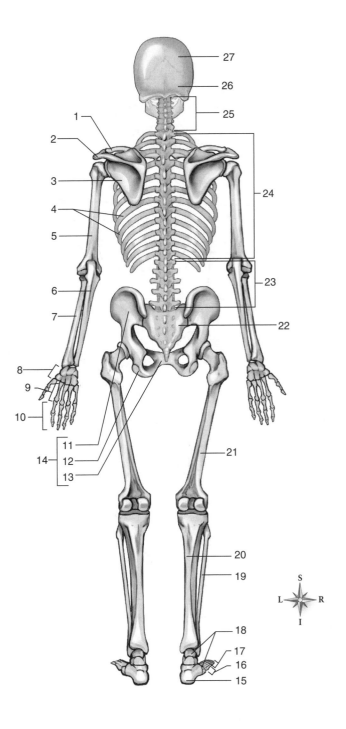

SKULL VIEWED FROM THE RIGHT SIDE

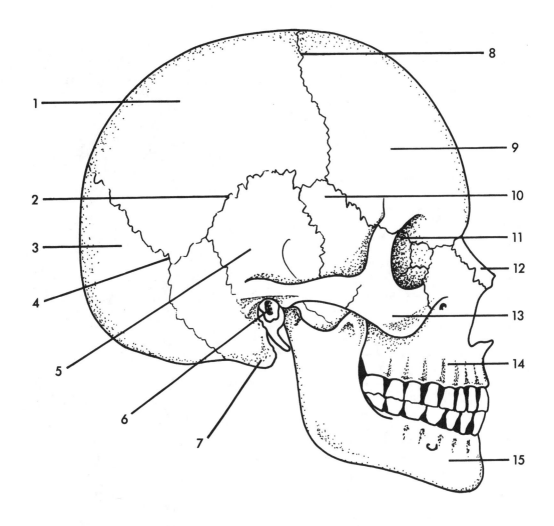

1. _____
2. _____
3. _____
4. _____
5. _____
6. _____
7. _____
8. _____

9. _____
10. _____
11. _____
12. _____
13. _____
14. _____
15. _____

SKULL VIEWED FROM THE FRONT

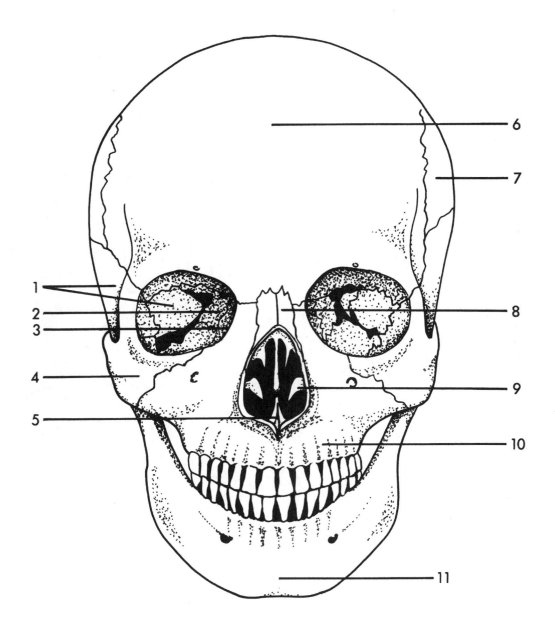

1. _____

2. _____

3. _____

4. _____

5. _____

6. _____

7. _____

8. _____

9. _____

10. _____

11. _____

STRUCTURE OF A DIARTHROTIC JOINT

1. _____

2. _____

3. _____

4. _____

5. _____

6. _____

7. _____

8. _____

9. _____

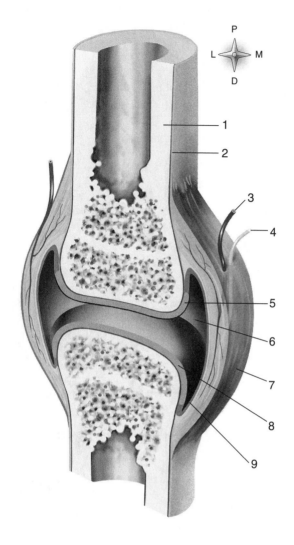

CHAPTER 8

The Muscular System

The muscular system is often referred to as the "power system," and rightfully so, because it is this system that provides the force necessary to move the body and perform many organ functions. Just as an automobile relies on the engine to provide motion, the body depends on the muscular system to perform both voluntary and involuntary movements. Walking, breathing, and the digestion of food are but a few examples of body functions that require the healthy performance of the muscular system.

Although this system has several functions, the primary purpose is to provide movement or power. Muscles produce power by contracting. The ability of a large muscle or muscle group to contract depends on the ability of microscopic muscle fibers to contract within the larger muscle. An understanding of these microscopic muscle fibers will assist you as you progress in your study to the larger muscles and muscle groups.

Muscle contractions may be one of several types: isotonic, isometric, twitch, or tetanic. When skeletal or voluntary muscles contract, they provide us with a variety of motions. Flexion, extension, abduction, adduction, and rotation are examples of these movements that provide us with both strength and agility.

Muscles are also used to keep the body healthy and in good condition. Scientific evidence keeps pointing to the fact that the proper use and exercise of muscles may prolong longevity. An understanding of the structure and function of the muscular system may, therefore, add quality and quantity to our lives.

TOPICS FOR REVIEW

Before progressing to Chapter 9, you should familiarize yourself with the structure and function of the three major types of muscle tissue. Your review should include the microscopic structure of skeletal muscle tissue, how a muscle is stimulated, the major types of skeletal muscle contractions, and the skeletal muscle groups. Your study should conclude with an understanding of the types of movements produced by skeletal muscle contractions and the major muscular disorders.

MUSCLE TISSUE

Match each descriptive word or phrase to its related muscle type and write the corresponding letter(s) in the answer blank.

A.   Skeletal muscle   B.   Cardiac muscle   C.   Smooth muscle

_____ 1.   Striated

_____ 2.   Cells branch frequently

_____ 3.   Moves food into the stomach

_____ 4.   Nonstriated

_____ 5.   Voluntary

_____ 6.   Keeps blood circulating through its vessels

_____ 7.   Involuntary

_____ 8.   Attaches to bone

_____ 9.   Hollow internal organs

_____ 10.   Visceral muscle

▶ *If you had difficulty with this section, review pages 207-208.*

STRUCTURE OF SKELETAL MUSCLES

Match each term on the left with its corresponding description on the right.

_____ 11.   Origin   A.   The muscle unit excluding the ends
_____ 12.   Insertion   B.   Attachment to the more movable bone
_____ 13.   Body   C.   Fluid-filled sacs
_____ 14.   Tendons   D.   Attachment to more stationary bone
_____ 15.   Bursae   E.   Anchor muscles to bones

MICROSCOPIC STRUCTURE

_____ 16.   Muscle fibers   A.   Protein that forms thick myofilaments
_____ 17.   Actin   B.   Basic functional unit of skeletal muscle
_____ 18.   Sarcomere   C.   Protein that forms thin myofilaments
_____ 19.   Myosin   D.   Microscopic threadlike structures found in skeletal muscle fibers
_____ 20.   Myofilaments   E.   Elongated contractile cells of muscle tissue

▶ *If you had difficulty with this section, review pages 208-211.*

FUNCTIONS OF SKELETAL MUSCLE

Fill in the blanks.

21. Muscles move bones by _____ on them.

22. As a rule, only the _____ bone moves.

23. The _____ bone moves toward the
_____ bone.

24. Of all the muscles contracting simultaneously, the one mainly responsible for producing a particular movement is called the _____ _____ for that movement.

25. As prime movers contract, other muscles called _____ relax.

26. The biceps brachii is the prime mover during flexing, and the brachialis is its helper or _____ muscle.

27. We are able to maintain our body position because of a specialized type of skeletal muscle contraction called _____ _____.

28. _____ _____ maintains body posture by counteracting the pull of gravity.

29. A decrease in temperature, a condition known as _____, will drastically affect cellular activity and normal body function.

30. Energy required to produce a muscle contraction is obtained from _____.

▶ *If you had difficulty with this section, review page 211.*

FATIGUE
ROLE OF OTHER BODY SYSTEMS
MOTOR UNIT
MUSCLE STIMULUS

If the statement is true, write "T" in the answer blank. If the statement is false, correct the statement by circling the incorrect term and writing the correct term in the answer blank.

_____ 31. The point of contact between the nerve ending and the muscle fiber is called a *motor neuron.*

_____ 32. A motor neuron together with the cells it innervates is called a *motor unit.*

_____ 33. If muscle cells are stimulated repeatedly without adequate periods of rest, the strength of the muscle contraction will decrease resulting in fatigue.

_____ 34. The depletion of oxygen in muscle cells during vigorous and prolonged exercise is known as *fatigue.*

_____ 35. An adequate stimulus will contract a muscle cell completely because of the "must" theory.

_____ 36. When oxygen supplies run low, muscle cells produce ATP and other waste products during contraction.

_____ 37. In a laboratory setting, a single muscle fiber can be isolated and subjected to stimuli of varying intensities so that it can be studied.

_____ 38. The minimal level of stimulation required to cause a fiber to contract is called the *threshold stimulus*.

_____ 39. Smooth muscles bring about movements by pulling on bones across movable joints.

_____ 40. A nervous system disorder that shuts off impulses to certain skeletal muscles may result in paralysis.

TYPES OF SKELETAL MUSCLE CONTRACTION

Circle the correct answer.

41. When a muscle contracts and no movement results, the contraction is:
    A. Isometric
    B. Isotonic
    C. Twitch
    D. Tetanic

42. Walking is an example of which type of contraction?
    A. Isometric
    B. Isotonic
    C. Twitch
    D. Tetanic

43. Pushing against a wall is an example of which type of contraction?
    A. Isotonic
    B. Isometric
    C. Twitch
    D. Tetanic

44. Endurance training is also known as:
    A. Isometrics
    B. Hypertrophy
    C. Aerobic training
    D. Strength training

45. Benefits of regular exercise include all of the following *except*:
    A. Improved lung functioning
    B. More efficient heart
    C. Less fatigue
    D. Atrophy

46. Twitch contractions easily can be seen:
    A. In isolated muscles prepared for research
    B. In a great deal of normal muscle activity
    C. During resting periods
    D. None of the above

47. Individual contractions "melt" together to produce a sustained contraction or:
    A. Twitch
    B. Tetanus
    C. Isotonic response
    D. Isometric response

48. In most cases, isotonic contraction of muscle produces movement at a/an:
    A. Insertion
    B. Beginning
    C. Joint
    D. Bursa

49. Prolonged inactivity causes muscles to shrink in mass, a condition called:
    A. Hypertrophy
    B. Disuse atrophy
    C. Paralysis
    D. Muscle fatigue

50. Muscle hypertrophy can be best enhanced by a program of:
    A. Isotonic exercise
    B. Better posture
    C. High-protein diet
    D. Strength training

▷ *If you have had difficulty with this section, review pages 211-216.*

SKELETAL MUSCLE GROUPS

Match the function(s) to the muscles listed below and write the corresponding letter(s) in the answer blank.

A. Flexor   C. Abductor   E. Rotator
B. Extensor   D. Adductor   F. Dorsiflexor or plantar flexor

_____ 51. Deltoid

_____ 52. Tibialis anterior

_____ 53. Gastrocnemius

_____ 54. Biceps brachii

_____ 55. Gluteus medius

_____ 56. Soleus

_____ 57. Iliopsoas

_____ 58. Pectoralis major

_____ 59. Gluteus maximus

_____ 60. Triceps brachii

_____ 61. Sternocleidomastoid

_____ 62. Trapezius

_____ 63. Gracilis

▶ *If you had difficulty with this section, review pages 216-221 and 223.*

MOVEMENTS PRODUCED BY SKELETAL MUSCLE CONTRACTIONS

Circle the correct answer.

64. A movement that makes the angle between two bones smaller is:
    A. Flexion
    B. Extension
    C. Abduction
    D. Adduction

65. Moving a part toward the midline is:
    A. Flexion
    B. Extension
    C. Abduction
    D. Adduction

66. Moving a part away from the midline is:
    A. Flexion
    B. Extension
    C. Abduction
    D. Adduction

67. When you move your head from side to side as in shaking your head "no," you are _____ a muscle group.
    A. Rotating
    B. Pronating
    C. Supinating
    D. Abducting

68. _____ occurs when you turn the palm of your hand from an anterior to posterior position.
    A. Dorsiflexion
    B. Plantar flexion
    C. Supination
    D. Pronation

69. *Dorsiflexion* refers to:
    A. Hand movements
    B. Eye movements
    C. Foot movements
    D. Head movements

▶ *If you had difficulty with this section, review pages 221-223.*

MAJOR MUSCULAR DISORDERS

Circle the correct answer.

70. Muscle strains are characterized by (*myalgia* or *fibromyositis*).

71. Crush injuries can cause (*hemoglobin* or *myoglobin*) to accumulate in the blood and result in kidney failure.

72. A viral infection of the nerves that controls skeletal muscle movement is known as (*poliomyelitis* or *muscular dystrophy*).

73. (*Muscular dystrophy* or *Myasthenia gravis*) is a group of genetic diseases characterized by atrophy of skeletal muscle tissues.

74. (*Muscular dystrophy* or *Myasthenia gravis*) is an autoimmune disease in which the immune system attacks muscle cells at the neuromuscular junction.

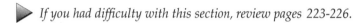 *If you had difficulty with this section, review pages 223-226.*

APPLYING WHAT YOU KNOW

75. Casey noticed pain whenever she reached for anything in her cupboards. Her doctor told her that the small fluid-filled sacs in her shoulder were inflamed. What condition did Casey have?

76. The nurse was preparing an injection for Mrs. Tatakis. The amount to be given was 2 mL. What area of the body will the nurse most likely select for administering this injection?

77. Chris was playing football and pulled a band of fibrous connective tissue that attached a muscle to a bone. What is the common term for this tissue?

78.   Word Find

Find and circle 25 muscle terms. Words may be spelled top to bottom, bottom to top, right to left, left to right, or diagonally.

```
G  A  S  T  R  O  C  N  E  M  I  U  S  D  U
M  S  G  I  O  N  O  I  S  N  E  T  X  E  U
U  R  N  N  T  O  M  S  R  B  S  F  D  T  T
S  U  I  S  C  I  B  O  N  T  P  N  E  A  R
C  B  R  E  U  X  V  T  O  O  E  C  L  I  A
L  Q  T  R  D  E  C  O  D  A  C  M  T  R  P
E  T  S  T  B  L  M  N  N  V  I  E  O  T  E
X  F  M  I  A  F  Y  I  E  Y  B  N  I  S  Z
S  I  A  O  V  I  E  C  T  L  S  S  D  I  I
S  Y  H  N  S  S  R  O  T  A  T  O  R  G  U
U  A  M  G  A  R  H  P  A  I  D  J  N  R  S
E  H  A  T  R  O  P  H  Y  L  N  J  T  E  B
L  N  O  H  T  D  E  U  G  I  T  A  F  N  T
O  R  I  G  I  N  O  S  N  V  S  B  Z  Y  L
S  B  V  T  O  J  C  T  R  I  C  E  P  S  S
```

Abductor	Flexion	Soleus
Atrophy	Gastrocnemius	Striated
Biceps	Hamstrings	Synergist
Bursa	Insertion	Tendon
Deltoid	Isometric	Tenosynovitis
Diaphragm	Isotonic	Trapezius
Dorsiflexion	Muscle	Triceps
Extension	Origin	
Fatigue	Rotator	

DID YOU KNOW?

If all of your muscles pulled in one direction, you would have the power to move 25 tons.

THE MUSCULAR SYSTEM

Fill in the crossword puzzle.

ACROSS

2. Shaking your head "no"
6. Muscle shrinkage
7. Toward the body's midline
9. Produces movement opposite to prime movers
12. Movement that makes joint angles larger
13. Small fluid-filled sac between tendons and bones

DOWN

1. Increase in size
3. Away from the body's midline
4. Turning your palm from an anterior to posterior position
5. Attachment to the more movable bone
7. Protein which composes myofilaments
8. Attachment to the more stationary bone
10. Assists prime movers with movement
11. Anchors muscles to bones

CHECK YOUR KNOWLEDGE

Multiple Choice

Circle the correct answer.

1. Which of the following statements about a motor unit is true?
   A. It consists of a muscle cell group and a motor neuron.
   B. The point of contact between the nerve ending and the muscle fiber is called the *neuromuscular junction*.
   C. Chemicals generate events within the muscle cell that result in contraction of the muscle cell.
   D. All of the above are true.

2. What is movement of a part away from the midline of the body called?
   A. Abduction
   B. Adduction
   C. Pronation
   D. Plantar flexion

3. According to the sliding filament theory of muscle contraction:
   A. Muscle fibers contain thin myofilaments made of a protein called *myosin*.
   B. Muscle fibers contain thick myofilaments made up of a protein called *actin*.
   C. Thin and thick myofilaments move toward each other to cause muscle contraction.
   D. All of the above are true.

4. Which of the following statements is true of the hamstring group of muscles?
   A. It includes the rectus femoris.
   B. It flexes the knee.
   C. It originates on the pubis.
   D. All of the above are true.

5. What happens if a given muscle cell is stimulated by a threshold stimulus?
   A. It shows an "all or none" response.
   B. It shows a tetanus response.
   C. It shows a subminimal response.
   D. None of the above is true.

6. Which of the following statements about oxygen debt is true?
   A. It is caused when excess oxygen is present in the environment.
   B. It causes lactic acid buildup and soreness in muscles.
   C. It can be replaced by slow, shallow breathing.
   D. All of the above are true.

7. What is a quick, jerky response of a given muscle to a single stimulus called?
   A. Isometric
   B. Lockjaw
   C. Tetanus
   D. Twitch

8. Which of the following statements about muscle atrophy is true?
   A. It decreases the size of a muscle.
   B. It increases the size of a muscle.
   C. Has no effect on muscle size.
   D. None of the above is true.

9. Which of the following occurs during isometric exercises?
   A. Muscle length remains the same.
   B. Muscle tension remains the same.
   C. Muscle length shortens.
   D. None of the above occurs.

10. Which of the following statements about skeletal muscle contraction is true?
    A. Its attachment to the more stationary bone is called its *origin*.
    B. Its attachment to the more moveable bone is called its *insertion*.
    C. Both A and B are true.
    D. None of the above is true.

True/False

If the statement is true, write "T" on the answer blank. If the statement is false, correct the statement by circling the incorrect term and writing the correct term in the answer blank.

_____ 11. When a part is moved toward the midline, it is called *adduction*.

_____ 12. In most cases, isotonic contraction of a muscle produces movement at a joint.

_____ 13. Dorsiflexion occurs when you turn the palm of your hand from an anterior to a posterior position.

_____ 14. Exercise may cause an increase in muscle size called *atrophy*.

_____ 15. Isotonic contraction is an example of a contraction used while walking.

_____ 16. If a muscle is overworked without sufficient rest, the result will be a decrease in muscle strength and fatigue.

_____ 17. A bone of insertion moves toward the bone of origin.

_____ 18. A condition in which the body temperature is drastically low is referred to as *hyperthermia*.

_____ 19. Tetanic contraction is caused by a series of rapid stimuli.

_____ 20. When the angle between two bones becomes smaller, it is called *extension*.

MUSCLES—ANTERIOR VIEW

1. _____

2. _____

3. _____

4. _____

5. _____

6. _____

7. _____

8. _____

9. _____

10. _____

11. _____

12. _____

13. _____

14. _____

15. _____

16. _____

17. _____

18. _____

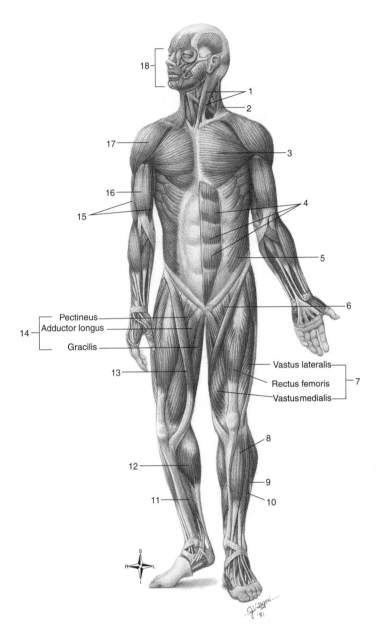

Pectineus

Adductor longus

Gracilis

Vastus lateralis

Rectus femoris

Vastus medialis

MUSCLES—POSTERIOR VIEW

1. _____

2. _____

3. _____

4. _____

5. _____

6. _____

7. _____

8. _____

9. _____

10. _____

11. _____

12. _____

13. _____

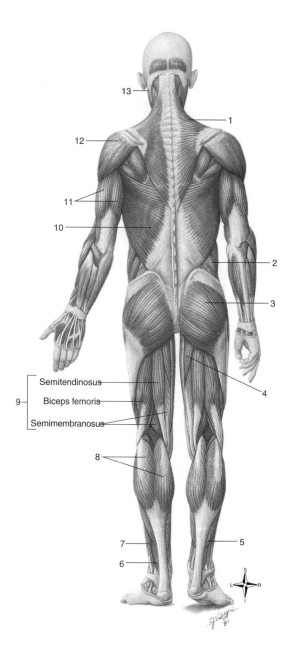

Semitendinosus

Biceps femoris

Semimembranosus

NEURON

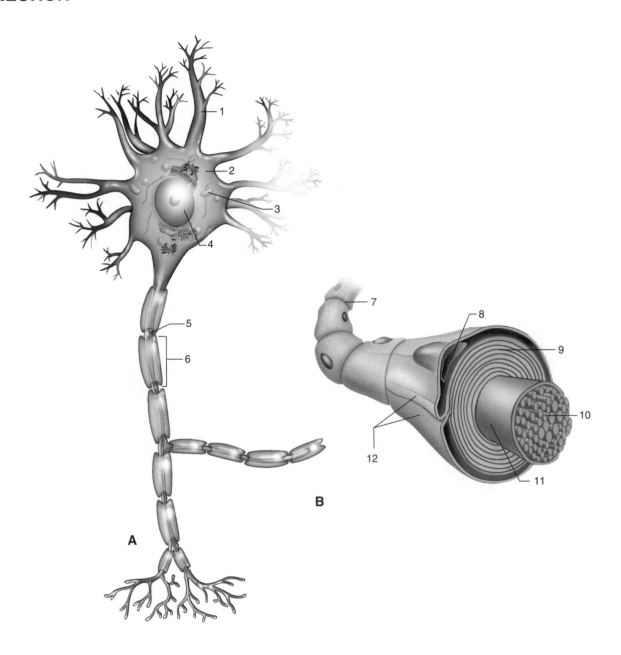

A

B

1. _____
2. _____
3. _____
4. _____
5. _____
6. _____

7. _____
8. _____
9. _____
10. _____
11. _____
12. _____

CRANIAL NERVES

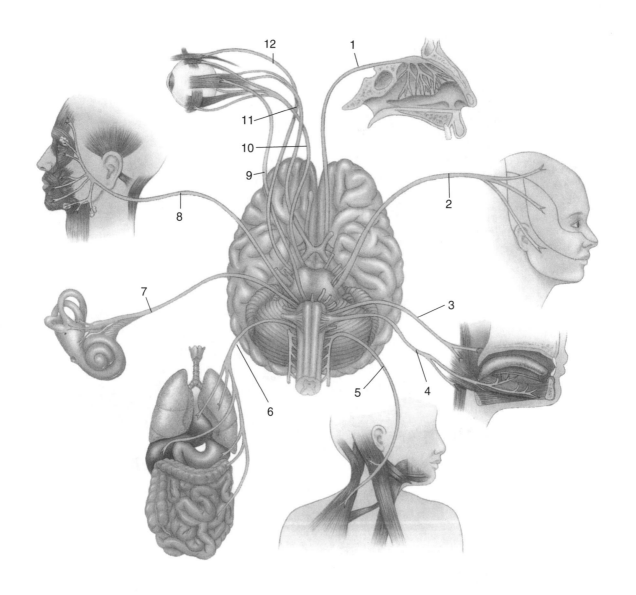

1. <u>Olfactory nerve</u>
2. <u>Trigeminal nerve</u>
3. (IX) <u>Glossopharyngeal nerve</u>
4. <u>Hypoglossal nerve (XII)</u>
5. <u>Accessory nerve (XI)</u>
6. <u>Vagus nerve (X)</u>

7. <u>Vestibulocochlear nerve (VIII)</u>
8. <u>Facial nerve (VII)</u>
9. <u>Abducens nerve (VI)</u>
10. <u>Oculomotor nerve (III)</u>
11. <u>Optic nerve</u>
12. <u>Trochlear nerve (IV)</u>

SAGITTAL SECTION OF THE CENTRAL NERVOUS SYSTEM

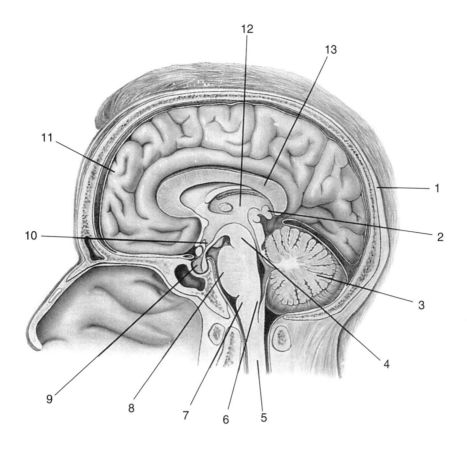

1. _____

2. _____

3. _____

4. _____

5. _____

6. _____

7. _____

8. _____

9. _____

10. _____

11. _____

12. _____

13. _____

THE CEREBRUM

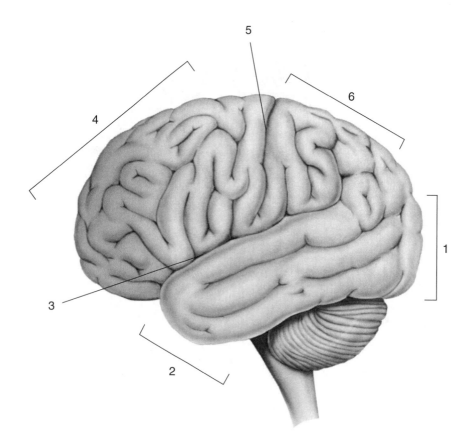

1. _____   4. _____

2. _____   5. _____

3. _____   6. _____

NEURON PATHWAYS

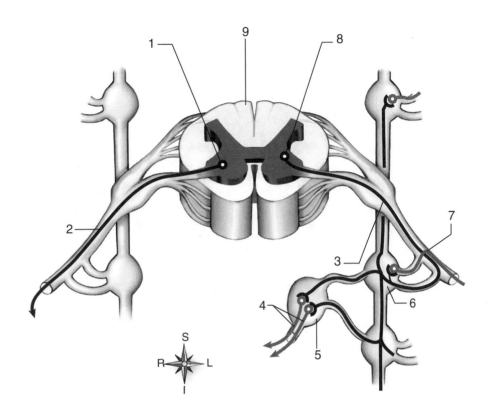

1. <u>Cell body of somatic</u>
   <u>Axon motor neuron</u>
2. <u>of somatic motor neuron</u>
   Axon of preganglionic
3. <u>Sympathetic neuron</u>
   Postganglionic neuron's
4. <u>axon</u>
5. <u>Collateral ganglion</u>

6. <u>Sympathetic ganglion</u>

7. <u>Cell body of preganglionic</u>
   <u>neuron</u>
8.
9. <u>spinal cord</u>

EAR

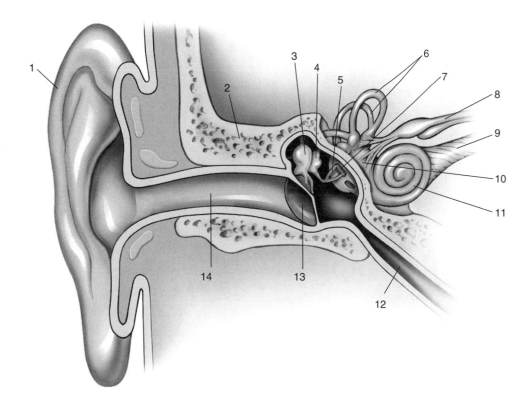

1. _____

2. _____

3. _____

4. _____

5. _____

6. _____

7. _____

8. _____

9. _____

10. _____

11. _____

12. _____

13. _____

14. _____

CHAPTER 11

The Endocrine System

The endocrine system is often compared to a fine concert symphony. When all instruments are playing properly, the sound is melodious. If one instrument plays too loud or too soft, however, it affects the overall quality of the entire performance.

The endocrine system is a ductless system that releases hormones into the bloodstream to help regulate body functions. The pituitary gland may be considered the conductor of the orchestra, because it stimulates many of the endocrine glands to secrete their powerful hormones. All hormones, whether stimulated in this manner or by other control mechanisms, are interdependent. A change in the level of one hormone may affect the level of many other hormones.

In addition to the endocrine glands, prostaglandins, or "tissue hormones," are powerful substances similar to hormones that have been found in a variety of body tissues. These hormones are often produced in a tissue and diffuse only a short distance to act on cells within that area. Prostaglandins influence respiration, blood pressure, gastrointestinal secretions, and the reproductive system and may some day play an important role in the treatment of diseases such as hypertension, asthma, and ulcers.

The endocrine system is a system of communication and control. It differs from the nervous system in that hormones provide a slower, longer-lasting effect than do nerve stimuli and responses. Your understanding of the "system of hormones" will give you a new awareness of the mechanism of our emotions, response to stress, growth, chemical balances, and many other body functions.

TOPICS FOR REVIEW

Before progressing to Chapter 12, you should be able to identify and locate the primary endocrine glands of the body. Your understanding should include the hormones that are produced by these glands and the method by which these secretions are regulated. Your study will conclude with the pathological conditions that result from the malfunction of this system.

MECHANISMS OF HORMONE ACTION
REGULATION OF HORMONE SECRETION
MECHANISMS OF ENDOCRINE DISEASE
PROSTAGLANDINS

Match each term on the left with the corresponding word or phrase on the right.

Group A

_____ 1. Pituitary

_____ 2. Parathyroids

_____ 3. Adrenals

_____ 4. Ovaries

_____ 5. Thymus

A. Pelvic cavity

B. Mediastinum

C. Neck

D. Cranial cavity

E. Abdominal cavity

Group B

_____ 6. Negative feedback

_____ 7. Tissue hormones

_____ 8. Polyendocrine disorders

_____ 9. Exocrine glands

_____ 10. Target organ cells

A. Result from hyposecretion or hypersecretion of several hormones

B. Respond to a particular hormone

C. Prostaglandins

D. Discharge secretions into ducts

E. Specialized homeostatic mechanism that regulates release of hormones

Fill in the blanks.

Nonsteroid hormones work according to the (11) _____

_____ mechanism. According to this concept, a

(12) _____ hormone acts as a (13) _____

_____, providing communication between endocrine glands and

(14) _____ _____. A second messenger,

such as (15) _____ _____, provides com-

munication within a hormone's (16) _____

_____. (17) _____

_____ disrupts the normal negative feedback control of hormones through-

out the body and may result in tissue damage, sterility, mental imbalance, and a host of life-threatening meta-

bolic problems.

▶ *If you had difficulty with this section, review pages 309-317.*

PITUITARY GLAND
HYPOTHALAMUS

Circle the correct answer.

18. The pituitary gland lies in the _____ bone.
    A. Ethmoid
    B. Sphenoid
    C. Temporal
    D. Frontal
    E. Occipital

19. Which one of the following structures would *not* be stimulated by a tropic hormone from the anterior pituitary?
    A. Ovaries
    B. Testes
    C. Thyroid
    D. Adrenals
    E. Uterus

20. Which one of the following is *not* a function of FSH?
    A. Stimulates the growth of follicles
    B. Stimulates the production of estrogens
    C. Stimulates the growth of seminiferous tubules
    D. Stimulates the interstitial cells of the testes

21. Which one of the following is *not* a function of LH?
    A. Stimulates maturation of a developing follicle
    B. Stimulates the production of estrogens
    C. Stimulates the formation of a corpus luteum
    D. Stimulates sperm cells to mature in the male
    E. Causes ovulation to occur

22. Which one of the following is *not* a function of GH?
    A. Increases glucose catabolism
    B. Increases fat catabolism
    C. Speeds up the movement of amino acids into cells from the bloodstream
    D. All of the above are functions of GH

23. Which one of the following hormones is *not* released by the anterior pituitary gland?
    A. ACTH
    B. TSH
    C. ADH
    D. FSH
    E. LH

24. Which one of the following is *not* a function of prolactin?
    A. Stimulates breast development during pregnancy
    B. Stimulates milk secretion after delivery
    C. Causes the release of milk from glandular cells of the breast
    D. All of the above are functions of prolactin

25. The anterior pituitary gland secretes:
    A. Eight major hormones
    B. Tropic hormones that stimulate other endocrine glands to grow and secrete
    C. ADH
    D. Oxytocin

26. TSH acts on the:
    A. Thyroid
    B. Thymus
    C. Pineal gland
    D. Testes

27. ACTH stimulates the:
    A. Adrenal cortex
    B. Adrenal medulla
    C. Hypothalamus
    D. Ovaries

28. Which hormone is secreted by the posterior pituitary gland?
    A. MSH
    B. LH
    C. GH
    D. ADH

29. ADH serves the body by:
    A. Initiating labor
    B. Accelerating water reabsorption from urine into the blood
    C. Stimulating the pineal gland
    D. Regulating the calcium/phosphorus levels in the blood

30. The disease caused by hyposecretion of ADH is:
    A. Diabetes insipidus
    B. Diabetes mellitus
    C. Acromegaly
    D. Myxedema

31. The actual production of ADH and oxytocin takes place in which area?
   A. Anterior pituitary
   B. Posterior pituitary
   C. Hypothalamus
   D. Pineal gland

32. Inhibiting hormones are produced by the:
   A. Anterior pituitary
   B. Posterior pituitary
   C. Hypothalamus
   D. Pineal gland

Match one of the glands listed with each numbered term and write the corresponding letter in the answer blank.

A.   Anterior pituitary   B.   Posterior pituitary   C.   Hypothalamus

_____ 33.   Adenohypophysis

_____ 34.   Neurohypophysis

_____ 35.   Induced labor

_____ 36.   Appetite

_____ 37.   Acromegaly

_____ 38.   Body temperature

_____ 39.   Sex hormones

_____ 40.   Tropic hormones

_____ 41.   Gigantism

_____ 42.   Releasing hormones

▶ *If you had difficulty with this section, review pages 317-320 and Table 11-1.*

THYROID GLAND

PARATHYROID GLANDS

Circle the correct answer.

43. The thyroid gland lies (*above* or *below*) the larynx.

44. The thyroid gland secretes (*calcitonin* or *glucagon*).

45. For thyroxine to be produced in adequate amounts, the diet must contain sufficient (*calcium* or *iodine*).

46. Most endocrine glands (*do* or *do not*) store their hormones.

47. Colloid is a storage medium for the (*thyroid* or *parathyroid*) hormone.

48. Calcitonin (*increases* or *decreases*) the concentration of calcium in the blood.

49. A goiter results from (*hyperthyroidism* or *hypothyroidism*).

50. Hyposecretion of thyroid hormones during the formative years leads to (*cretinism* or *myxedema*).

51. The parathyroid glands secrete the hormone (*PTH* or *PTA*).

52. Parathyroid hormone tends to (*increase* or *decrease*) the concentration of calcium in the blood.

▶ *If you had difficulty with this section, review pages 320-323.*

ADRENAL GLANDS

Fill in the blanks.

53. The adrenal gland is actually two separate endocrine glands, the _____ _____ and the _____ _____.

54. Hormones secreted by the adrenal cortex are known as _____.

55. The outer zone of the adrenal cortex, the zona glomerulosa, secretes _____.

56. The middle zone, the zona fasciculata, secretes _____.

57. The innermost zone, the zona reticularis, secretes _____ _____.

58. Glucocorticoids act in several ways to increase _____.

59. Glucocorticoids also play an essential part in maintaining _____ _____.

60. The adrenal medulla secretes the hormones _____ and _____.

61. The adrenal glands may help the body resist _____.

62. A _____ tumor of the adrenal cortex causes masculinizing symptoms to appear in a woman.

Match each of numbered terms with the related adrenal structure and write the corresponding letter in the answer blank.

A. Adrenal cortex   B. Adrenal medulla

_____ 63.   Addison disease

_____ 64.   Anti-immunity

_____ 65.   Adrenaline

_____ 66.   Cushing syndrome

_____ 67.   Fight-or-flight syndrome

_____ 68.   Aldosterone

_____ 69.   Androgens

▶ *If you had difficulty with this section, review pages 323-328.*

PANCREATIC ISLETS
SEX GLANDS
THYMUS
PLACENTA
PINEAL GLAND

Circle the word in each word group that does not belong.

70. Alpha cells	Glucagon	Beta cells	Glycogenolysis
71. Insulin	Glucagon	Beta cells	Diabetes mellitus
72. Estrogens	Progesterone	Corpus luteum	Thymosin
73. Chorion	Interstitial cells	Testosterone	Semen
74. Immune system	Mediastinum	Aldosterone	Thymosin
75. Pregnancy	ACTH	Estrogen	Chorion
76. Melatonin	Sleep cycle	"Third eye"	Semen

Match each term on the left with the corresponding hormone on the right.

Group A

_____ 77.	Alpha cells	A.	Estrogen
_____ 78.	Beta cells	B.	Progesterone
_____ 79.	Corpus luteum	C.	Insulin
_____ 80.	Interstitial cells	D.	Testosterone
_____ 81.	Ovarian follicles	E.	Glucagon

Group B

_____ 82.	Placenta	A.	Melatonin
_____ 83.	Pineal gland	B.	ANH
_____ 84.	Heart atria	C.	Testosterone
_____ 85.	Testes	D.	Thymosin
_____ 86.	Thymus	E.	Chorionic gonadotropin

▷ *If you had difficulty with this section, review pages 328-332.*

UNSCRAMBLE THE WORDS

87. **R O O D I I T S C C**

88. **S I U I S E R D**

89. **U O O O T D C S I I L R C C G**

90. **R I O D S T E S**

Take the circled letters, unscramble them, and fill in the solution.

Why Billy didn't like to take exams.

91.

APPLYING WHAT YOU KNOW

92. Mrs. Tips made a routine visit to her physician last week. When the laboratory results came back, the report indicated a high level of chorionic gonadotropin in her urine. What did this mean to Mrs. Tips?

93. Mrs. Wilcox noticed that her daughter was beginning to take on the secondary sex characteristics of a male. The pediatrician diagnosed the condition as a tumor of an endocrine gland. Where specifically was the tumor located?

94. Mrs. Liddy was pregnant and was 2 weeks past her due date. Her doctor suggested that she enter the hospital and he would induce labor. What hormone will he give Mrs. Liddy?

95. Word Find

Find and circle 16 terms presented in this chapter. Words may be spelled top to bottom, bottom to top, right to left, left to right, or diagonally.

```
S  S  I  S  E  R  U  I  D  M  E  S  I  T  W
N  D  N  X  E  B  A  M  E  D  E  X  Y  M  I
I  I  G  O  N  R  S  G  X  T  I  I  Y  V  B
D  O  M  S  I  N  I  T  E  R  C  C  U  Q  D
N  C  X  S  R  T  N  B  O  T  V  M  Y  O  M
A  I  M  E  C  L  A  C  R  E  P  Y  H  I  X
L  T  Y  R  O  I  E  Z  Q  R  T  J  V  K  F
G  R  E  T  D  P  S  N  I  L  D  J  M  X  N
A  O  O  S  N  I  D  K  I  N  K  S  P  P  O
T  C  P  R  E  T  I  O  G  R  I  F  M  X  G
S  L  M  H  Y  P  O  G  L  Y  C  E  M  I  A
O  A  J  L  H  O  R  M  O  N  E  O  T  G  C
R  C  E  L  T  S  E  L  C  N  P  N  X  U  U
P  I  O  S  W  R  T  X  C  G  U  L  O  E  L
G  G  V  Y  H  M  S  H  Y  K  A  K  N  Q  G
```

Corticoids Glucagon   Myxedema
Cretinism   Goiter   Prostaglandins
Diabetes   Hormone   Steroids
Diuresis   Hypercalcemia Stress
Endocrine   Hypoglycemia
Exocrine   Luteinization

DID YOU KNOW?

The total daily output of the pituitary gland is less than 1/1,000,000 of a gram, yet this small amount is responsible for stimulating the majority of all endocrine functions.

THE ENDOCRINE SYSTEM

Fill in the crossword puzzle.

ACROSS

1. Secreted by cells in the walls of the heart's atria
4. Adrenal medulla
6. Estrogens
8. Converts amino acids to glucose
9. Melanin
11. Labor

DOWN

2. Hypersecretion of insulin
3. Antagonist to diuresis
5. Increases calcium concentration
7. Hyposecretion of islets of Langerhans (one word)
8. Hyposecretion of thyroid
10. Adrenal cortex

CHECK YOUR KNOWLEDGE

Multiple Choice

Circle the correct answer.

1. What does the outer zone of the adrenal cortex secrete?
   A. Mineralocorticoids
   B. Sex hormones
   C. Glucocorticoids
   D. Epinephrine

2. From what condition does diabetes insipidus result?
   A. Low insulin levels
   B. High glucagon levels
   C. Low antidiuretic hormone levels
   D. High steroid levels

3. Which of the following statements is true regarding a young child whose growth is stunted, metabolism is low, sexual development is delayed, and mental development is retarded?
   A. The child suffers from cretinism.
   B. The child has an underactive thyroid.
   C. The child could suffer from a pituitary disorder.
   D. All of the above are true.

4. What can result when too much growth hormone is produced by the pituitary gland?
   A. Hyperglycemia
   B. A pituitary giant
   C. Both A and B
   D. None of the above

5. Which of the following glands is *not* regulated by the pituitary?
   A. Thyroid
   B. Ovaries
   C. Adrenals
   D. Thymus

6. Which of the following statements about the antidiuretic hormone is true?
   A. It is released by the posterior lobe of the pituitary.
   B. It causes diabetes insipidus when produced in insufficient amounts.
   C. It decreases urine volume.
   D. All of the above are true.

7. What controls the development of the body's immune system?
   A. Pituitary
   B. Thymus
   C. Pineal body
   D. Thyroid

8. Administration of what would best treat a person suffering from severe allergies?
   A. Gonadocorticoids
   B. Glucagon
   C. Mineralocorticoids
   D. Glucocorticoids

9. What endocrine gland is composed of cell clusters called the *islets of Langerhans*?
   A. Adrenals
   B. Thyroid
   C. Pituitary
   D. Pancreas

10. Which of the following statements concerning prostaglandins is true?
    A. They control activities of widely separated organs.
    B. They can be called *tissue hormones*.
    C. They diffuse over long distances to act on cells.
    D. All of the above are true.

Matching

Match each term in column A with the corresponding hormone in column B. (Only one answer is correct for each.)

Column A

_____ 11. Goiter

_____ 12. Ovulation

_____ 13. Diabetes mellitus

_____ 14. Lactation

_____ 15. Diabetes insipidus

_____ 16. Chorionic gonadotropins

_____ 17. Cushing syndrome

_____ 18. Labor

_____ 19. Acromegaly

_____ 20. Hypercalcemia

Column B

A. Glucocorticoid hormones

B. Antidiuretic hormone

C. Calcitonin

D. Oxytocin

E. Growth hormone

F. Placenta

G. Luteinizing hormone

H. Insulin

I. Prolactin

J. Thyroid hormones

ENDOCRINE GLANDS

1. _____

2. _____

3. _____

4. _____

5. _____

6. _____

7. _____

8. _____

9. _____

10. _____

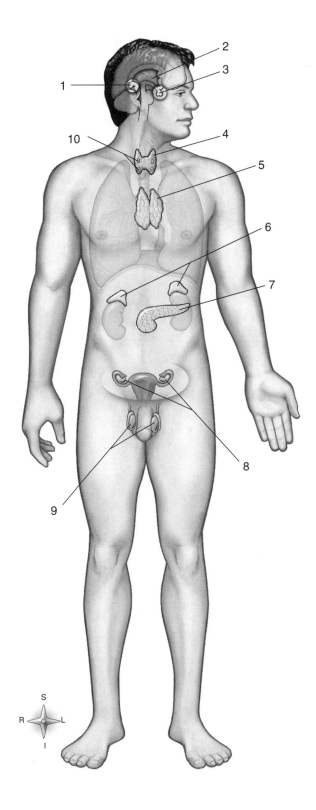

CHAPTER 12

Blood

Blood, the river of life, is the body's primary means of internal transportation. Although it is the respiratory system that provides oxygen for the body, the digestive system that provides nutrients, and the urinary system that eliminates wastes, none of these functions could be provided for the individual cells without blood. In less than 1 minute, a drop of blood will complete a trip through the entire body, distributing nutrients and collecting the wastes of metabolism.

Blood is divided into plasma (the liquid portion of blood) and the formed elements (the blood cells). There are three types of blood cells: red blood cells, white blood cells, and platelets. Together these cells and plasma provide a means of transportation that delivers the body's daily necessities.

Although all of us have red blood cells that are similar in shape, we have different blood types. Blood types are identified by the presence of certain antigens in the red blood cells. Every person's blood belongs to one of four main blood groups: Type A, B, AB, or O. Any one of the four groups or "types" may or may not have the Rh factor present in the red blood cells. If an individual has a specific antigen called the Rh factor present in his or her blood, the blood is Rh positive. If this factor is missing, the blood is Rh negative. Approximately 85% of the population has the Rh factor (Rh positive), whereas 15% do not have the Rh factor (Rh negative).

Your understanding of this chapter will be necessary to prepare a proper foundation for learning about the circulatory system.

TOPICS FOR REVIEW

Before progressing to Chapter 13, you should have an understanding of the structure and function of blood plasma and cells. Your review should also include an understanding of blood types and Rh factors.

BLOOD COMPOSITION

Circle the correct answer.

1. Which one of the following substances is *not* a part of the plasma?
   A. Water
   B. Proteins
   C. Nutrients
   D. Waste products
   E. Formed elements

2. The normal volume of blood in an adult is approximately:
   A. 2-3 pints
   B. 2-3 quarts
   C. 2-3 gallons
   D. 4-6 liters

3. Blood is normally:
   A. Very acidic
   B. Slightly acidic
   C. Neutral
   D. Slightly alkaline

4. PolyHeme is a/an:
   A. Artificial blood
   B. Antigen
   C. Antibody
   D. Plasma volume expander

5. Donated blood:
   A. Must be "typed and cross matched"
   B. Can be stored for only 6 weeks
   C. Is most valuable during the "golden hour"
   D. All of the above

▷ *If you had difficulty with this section, review pages 341-343.*

BLOOD TYPES

6. Fill in the blank areas.

Blood Type	Antigen Present in RBC	Antibody Present in Plasma
A		Anti-B
B	B	
AB		None
O	None	

Fill in the blanks.

7. An _____ is a substance that can stimulate the body to make antibodies.

8. An _____ is a substance made by the body in response to stimulation by an antigen.

9. Many antibodies react with their antigens to clump or _____ them.

10. If a baby is born to an Rh-negative mother and Rh-positive father, it may develop the disease _____ _____.

11. The term "Rh" is used because the antigen was first discovered in the blood of a _____ _____.

12. The universal donor blood is _____.

13. The universal recipient blood is _____.

▷ *If you had difficulty with this section, review pages 343-345.*

BLOOD PLASMA AND FORMED ELEMENTS

Circle the correct answer.

14. Another name for white blood cells is:
    A. Erythrocytes
    B. Leukocytes
    C. Thrombocytes
    D. Platelets

15. Another name for platelets is:
    A. Neutrophils
    B. Eosinophils
    C. Thrombocytes
    D. Erythrocytes

16. Pernicious anemia is caused by:
    A. A lack of vitamin B_{12}
    B. Hemorrhage
    C. Radiation
    D. Bleeding ulcers

17. The laboratory test called *hematocrit* tells the physician the volume of:
    A. White cells in a blood sample
    B. Red cells in a blood sample
    C. Platelets in a blood sample
    D. Plasma in a blood sample

18. An example of a nongranular leukocyte is a/an:
    A. Platelet
    B. Erythrocyte
    C. Eosinophil
    D. Monocyte

19. An excess of red blood cells is known as:
    A. Erythropenia
    B. Erythroplasia
    C. Polycythemia
    D. Anemia

20. A critical component of hemoglobin is:
    A. Potassium
    B. Calcium
    C. Vitamin K
    D. Iron

21. Sickle cell anemia is caused by:
    A. The production of an abnormal type of hemoglobin
    B. The production of excessive neutrophils
    C. The production of excessive platelets
    D. The production of abnormal leukocytes

22. The practice of using blood transfusions to increase oxygen delivery to muscles during athletic events is called:
    A. Blood antigen
    B. Blood doping
    C. Blood agglutination
    D. Blood proofing

23. One of the most useful and frequently performed clinical blood tests is called the:
    A. WBC
    B. CBC
    C. RBC
    D. Hematocrit

24. Which one of the following types of cells is not a granular leukocyte?
    A. Neutrophil
    B. Monocyte
    C. Basophil
    D. Eosinophil

25. If a blood cell has no nucleus and is shaped like a biconcave disc, then the cell most likely is a/an:
    A. Platelet
    B. Lymphocyte
    C. Basophil
    D. Eosinophil
    E. Red blood cell

26. Red bone marrow forms all kinds of blood cells except some:
    A. Platelets and basophils
    B. Lymphocytes and monocytes
    C. Red blood cells
    D. Neutrophils and eosinophils

27. Myeloid tissue is found in all but which one of the following locations?
    A. Sternum
    B. Ribs
    C. Wrist bones
    D. Hip bones
    E. Cranial bones

28. Lymphatic tissue is found in which of the following locations?
    A. Lymph nodes
    B. Thymus
    C. Spleen
    D. All of the above contain lymphatic tissue.

29. The "buffy coat" layer in a hematocrit tube contains:
    A. Red blood cells and platelets
    B. Plasma only
    C. Platelets only
    D. White blood cells and platelets
    E. None of the above is correct.

30. The hematocrit value for red blood cells is
    _____%.
    A. 75
    B. 60
    C. 50
    D. 45
    E. 35

31. An unusually low white blood cell count would be termed:
    A. Leukemia
    B. Leukopenia
    C. Leukocytosis
    D. Anemia
    E. None of the above is correct.

32. Most of the oxygen transported in the blood is carried by:
    A. Platelets
    B. Plasma
    C. White blood cells
    D. Red blood cells
    E. None of the above is correct.

33. The most numerous of the phagocytes are the
    _____.
    A. Lymphocytes
    B. Neutrophils
    C. Basophils
    D. Eosinophils
    E. Monocytes

34. Which one of the following types of cells is *not* phagocytic?
    A. Neutrophils
    B. Eosinophils
    C. Lymphocytes
    D. Monocytes
    E. All of the above are phagocytic cells.

35. Which of the following cell types functions in the immune process?
    A. Neutrophils
    B. Lymphocytes
    C. Monocytes
    D. Basophils
    E. Reticuloendothelial cells

36. Vitamin K stimulates liver cells to increase the synthesis of:
    A. Prothrombin
    B. Thrombin
    C. Platelets
    D. Heparin
    E. Calcium

37. If part of a clot dislodges and circulates through the bloodstream, the dislodged part is called a/an:
    A. Thrombus
    B. Thrombosis
    C. Anticoagulant
    D. Clotting factor
    E. Embolus

38. This disease usually occurs as a result of the destruction of bone marrow by toxic chemicals or radiation.
    A. Folate-deficiency anemia
    B. Aplastic anemia
    C. Hemolytic anemia
    D. Sickle cell anemia

39. An example of a hemolytic anemia is:
    A. Folate-deficiency anemia
    B. Aplastic anemia
    C. Sickle cell anemia
    D. Pernicious anemia

40. The disease that results from a failure to form blood clotting factor VIII is:
    A. Hemophilia
    B. Thrombocytopenia
    C. Thrombophlebitis
    D. None of the above

41. A special type of white blood cell count used as a diagnostic tool is known as a/an:
    A. Leukopenia
    B. Granulocyte count
    C. Differential WBC count
    D. CBC

▶ *If you had difficulty with this section, review pages 345-364.*

APPLYING WHAT YOU KNOW

42. Mrs. Florez's blood type is O positive. Her husband's type is O negative. Her newborn baby's blood type is O negative. Is there any need for concern with this combination?

43. After Mrs. Freund's baby was born, the doctor applied a gauze dressing for a short time on the umbilical cord. He also gave the baby a dose of vitamin K. Why did the doctor perform these two procedures?

44. Valerie was a teenager with a picky appetite. She loved junk food and seldom ate properly. She complained of being tired all the time. A visit to her doctor revealed a hemoglobin of 10 and RBCs that are classified as hypochromic. What condition does Valerie have?

45. Word Find

Find and circle 24 terms presented in this chapter. Words may be spelled top to bottom, bottom to top, right to left, left to right, or diagonally.

```
H S H K L S U L O B M E A E S
K E E V M Z H E P A R I N D N
D T M F A C T O R Y E T I Q P
O Y A O H N B A T Q Y A R A R
N C T J G W E H N P N L B U D
O O O S Q L R M E T I S I P M
R K C E M O O N I H I Q F W W
H U R T C N I B P A S G Z T G
E E I Y O B O O I V E W E T X
S L T C M D S E C N R T U N R
U E Y O Y A I M E K U E L Y S
S T R G B S T H R O M B U S Q
E H Z A M S A L P N D Z P O N
T E N H F P D A P M E E I B W
E W B P H K B O N C K W X V J
```

AIDS	Factor	Phagocytes
Anemia	Fibrin	Plasma
Antibody	Hematocrit	Recipient
Antigen	Hemoglobin	Rhesus
Basophil	Heparin	Serum
Donor	Leukemia	Thrombin
Embolus	Leukocytes	Thrombus
Erythrocytes	Monocyte	Type

BLOOD

Fill in the crossword puzzle.

ACROSS

1. Abnormally high WBC count
4. Final stage of clotting process
6. Oxygen-carrying mechanism of blood
9. To engulf and digest microbes
10. Stationary blood clot
12. RBC
13. Circulating blood clot
14. Liquid portion of blood

DOWN

2. Type O (two words)
3. Substances that stimulate the body to make antibodies
5. Type of leukocyte
7. Platelets
8. Prevents clotting of blood
11. Inability of the blood to carry sufficient oxygen

DID YOU KNOW?

Blood products are good for approximately 3 to 6 weeks, but fresh frozen plasma is good for at least 6 months.

CHECK YOUR KNOWLEDGE

Multiple Choice

Circle the correct answer.

1. Which of the following statements is false?
   A. Sickle cell anemia is caused by a genetic defect.
   B. Leukemia is characterized by a low number of WBCs.
   C. Polycythemia is characterized by an abnormally high number of erythrocytes.
   D. Pernicious anemia is caused by a lack of vitamin B_{12}.

2. Deficiency in the number or function of erythrocytes is called:
   A. Leukemia
   B. Anemia
   C. Polycythemia
   D. Leukopenia

3. Which of the following statements does *not* describe a characteristic of leukocytes?
   A. They are disk-shaped cells that do not contain a nucleus.
   B. They have the ability to fight infection.
   C. They provide defense against certain parasites.
   D. They provide immune defense.

4. Which of the following substances is *not* found in serum?
   A. Clotting factors
   B. Water
   C. Hormones
   D. All of the above substances are found in serum.

5. Which of the following substances is *not* found in blood plasma?
   A. Albumins
   B. Gases
   C. Waste products
   D. All of the above substances are found in blood plasma.

6. An allergic reaction may increase the number of:
   A. Eosinophils
   B. Neutrophils
   C. Lymphocytes
   D. Monocytes

7. What is a blood clot that is moving through the body called?
   A. Embolism
   B. Fibrosis
   C. Heparin
   D. Thrombosis

8. When could difficulty with the Rh blood factor arise?
   A. When an Rh-negative man and woman produce a child.
   B. When an Rh-positive man and woman produce a child.
   C. When an Rh-positive woman and an Rh-negative man produce a child.
   D. When an Rh-negative woman and an Rh-positive man produce a child.

9. What is the primary function of hemoglobin?
   A. To fight infection
   B. To make blood clots
   C. To carry oxygen
   D. To transport hormones

10. Which of the following steps are *not* involved in blood clot formation?
    A. A blood vessel is injured and platelet factors are formed.
    B. Thrombin is converted into prothrombin.
    C. Fibrinogen is converted into fibrin.
    D. All of the above are involved in blood clot formation.

Matching

Match each term in column A with its corresponding term or description in column B. (Only one answer is correct for each.)

Column A

_____ 11. Lymphocytes

_____ 12. Erythrocytes

_____ 13. Type AB

_____ 14. Basophils

_____ 15. Leukemia

_____ 16. Platelets

_____ 17. Type O

_____ 18. Rh factor

_____ 19. Red bone marrow

_____ 20. Neutrophils

Column B

A. Heparin

B. Contains anti-A and anti-B antibodies

C. Clotting

D. Immunity

E. Erythroblastosis fetalis

F. Anemia

G. Cancer

H. Contains A and B antigens

I. Myeloid tissue

J. Phagocytosis

HUMAN BLOOD CELLS

Fill in the missing areas of the table.

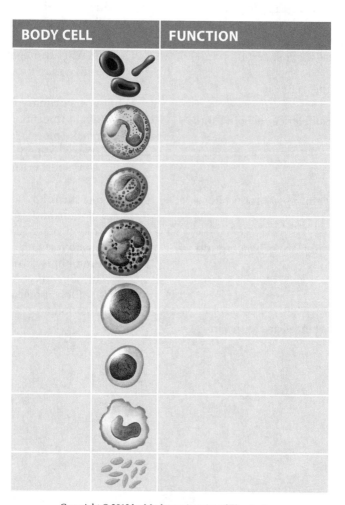

BODY CELL	FUNCTION

BLOOD TYPING

Using the key below, draw the appropriate reaction with the donor's blood in the circles.

Recipient's blood		Reactions with donor's blood			
RBC antigens	Plasma antibodies	Donor type O	Donor type A	Donor type B	Donor type AB
None (Type O)	Anti-A Anti-B	◯	◯	◯	◯
A (Type A)	Anti-B	◯	◯	◯	◯
B (Type B)	Anti-A	◯	◯	◯	◯
AB (Type AB)	(none)	◯	◯	◯	◯

 Normal blood    Agglutinated blood

CHAPTER 13

The Heart and Heart Disease

T he heart is actually two pumps—one moves blood to the lungs, the other pushes it out into the body. These two functions seem rather elementary in comparison to the complex and numerous functions performed by most of the other body organs, and yet if this pump stops, within a few short minutes all life ceases.

The heart is divided into two upper compartments called *atria*, or receiving chambers, and two lower compartments, or discharging chambers, called *ventricles*. By age 45, approximately 300,000 tons of blood will have passed through these chambers to be circulated to the blood vessels. This closed system of circulation provides distribution of blood to the entire body (systemic circulation) and to specific regions, such as the pulmonary circulation or coronary circulation.

The beating of the heart must be coordinated in a rhythmic manner if the heart is to pump effectively. This is achieved by electrical impulses that are stimulated by specialized structures embedded in the walls of the heart. The sinoatrial node, atrioventricular node, bundle of His, and Purkinje fibers combine efforts to conduct the tiny electrical currents necessary to contract the heart. Any interruption or failure of this system may result in serious pathology or death.

A healthy heart is necessary to pump sufficient blood throughout the body to nourish and oxygenate cells continuously. Your review of this chapter will provide you with an understanding of this vital organ that is necessary for survival.

TOPICS FOR REVIEW

Before progressing to Chapter 14, you should have an understanding of the structure and function of the heart. Your review should include a study of the coronary circulation and the conduction system of the heart. Your study should conclude with an understanding of the major coronary diseases and disorders.

LOCATION, SIZE, AND POSITION OF THE HEART

ANATOMY OF THE HEART

Fill in the blanks.

1. The system that supplies our cells' transportation needs is the

   _____ _____.

2. The _____ or blunt point at the lower edge of the heart lies on the diaphragm, pointing to the left.

3. The _____ _____ divides the heart into right and left sides between the atria.

4. The _____ are the two upper chambers of the heart.

5. The _____ are the two lower chambers of the heart.

6. The cardiac muscle tissue is referred to as the _____.

7. Inflammation of the heart lining is _____.

8. The two AV valves are _____ and _____.

9. The inner layer of the pericardium is called the _____ _____ or _____.

10. The outer layer of pericardium is called _____ _____.

11. If the pericardium becomes inflamed, a condition called _____ results.

12. The _____ _____ are located between the two ventricular chambers and the large arteries that carry blood away from the heart when contraction occurs.

13. A _____ _____ _____ is a condition caused when the flaps of this valve extend back into the left atrium, causing the valve to leak.

14. _____ _____ _____ is cardiac damage resulting from a delayed inflammatory response to a streptococcal infection that occurs most often in children.

▶ *If you had difficulty with this section, review pages 373-379.*

HEART SOUNDS
BLOOD FLOW THROUGH THE HEART
CORONARY CIRCULATION AND CORONARY HEART DISEASE
HEART FAILURE

Select the term that best matches each of the numbered descriptions. Write the corresponding letter in the answer blank.

_____ 15. Movement of blood from the left ventricle through the body

_____ 16. Blood clot

_____ 17. Myocardial infarction

_____ 18. Abnormal heart sound often caused by disorders of the valves

_____ 19. Movement of blood from the right ventricle to the lungs

_____ 20. Hardening of the arteries

_____ 21. Severe chest pain

_____ 22. High blood pressure

_____ 23. Structures through which blood returns to the left atrium

_____ 24. Treatment for certain coronary disorders

A. Heart murmur

B. Pulmonary circulation

C. Embolism

D. Heart attack

E. Angina pectoris

F. Systemic circulation

G. Atherosclerosis

H. Hypertension

I. Coronary bypass

J. Pulmonary veins

CARDIAC CYCLE
CONDUCTION SYSTEM OF THE HEART

Circle the correct answer.

25. The heart beats at an average rate of _____ beats per minute.
    A. 50
    B. 72
    C. 100
    D. 120

26. Each complete beat of the heart is called:
    A. Cardiac output
    B. Stroke volume
    C. A cardiac cycle
    D. A contraction

27. The pacemaker of the heart is also known as the:
    A. SA node
    B. AV node
    C. AV bundle
    D. Purkinje fibers

28. A rapid heart rhythm, over 100 beats per minutes, is referred to as:
    A. Bradycardia
    B. Sinus arrhythmia
    C. Tachycardia
    D. Premature contractions

29. The term _____ describes the electrical activity that triggers contraction of the heart muscle.
    A. Depolarization
    B. Repolarization
    C. AV node block
    D. Cardiac arrhythmia

30. A diagnostic tool that uses ultrasound to detect valve and heart disorders is known as a/an:
    A. Electrocardiogram
    B. Pacemaker
    C. TPA
    D. Echocardiogram

31. Frequent premature contractions can lead to:
    A. Extra systoles
    B. Bradycardia
    C. Fibrillation
    D. Heart failure

32. A drug that slows and increases the strength of cardiac contractions is:
    A. Digitalis
    B. Nitroglycerin
    C. Calcium-channel blocker
    D. Anticoagulant

33. Congestive heart failure inevitably causes:
    A. Extra systole
    B. Pulmonary edema
    C. Fibrillation
    D. Bradycardia

34. Failure of the right side of the heart due to blockage of pulmonary blood flow is called:
    A. Cardiomyopathy
    B. Ventricular fibrillation
    C. Cor pulmonale
    D. TPA

35. A nonmedical rescuer can defibrillate a victim in ventricular fibrillation with the use of a/an:
    A. AED
    B. Beta-blocker
    C. Demand pacemaker
    D. ECG

36. Coumadin and dicumarol are examples of commonly used oral:
    A. Beta-blockers
    B. Nitroglycerines
    C. Calcium-channel blockers
    D. Anticoagulants

▶ *If you had difficulty with this section review pages 379-389.*

UNSCRAMBLE THE WORDS

37. **CTSSYMEI**

☐◯☐◯☐☐☐

38. **LMTRIA**

◯☐☐☐☐

39. **THREA**

◯☐◯☐

40. **SBTUMHOR**

☐◯☐☐☐☐☐

Take the circled letters, unscramble them, and fill in the solution.

What Tom lacked on the dance floor.

41. ☐☐☐☐☐☐

APPLYING WHAT YOU KNOW

42. Else was experiencing angina pectoris. Her doctor suggested a surgical procedure that would require the removal of a vein from another region of her body, which would then be used to bypass a partial blockage in her coronary arteries. What is this procedure called?

43. Phil has a heart block. His electrical impulses are being blocked and prevented from reaching the ventricles. An electrical device that causes ventricular contractions at a rate necessary to maintain circulation is being considered as possible treatment for his condition. What is this device?

44. Mrs. Haygood was diagnosed with an acute case of endocarditis. What is the real danger of this diagnosis?

45. Jeanne's homework assignment was to demonstrate knowledge of the path of blood flow through the heart. Can you help her?

    Trace the blood flow through the heart by numbering the following structures in the correct sequence. Start with number 1, the vena cava, where blood enters the heart, and proceed until you have numbered all 12 structures.

    _____ Tricuspid valve   _____ Pulmonary veins

    _____ Pulmonary arteries   _____ Pulmonary semilunar valve

    _____ Bicuspid valve   _____ Left ventricle

    _____ Vena cava   _____ Right atrium

    _____ Right ventricle   _____ Left atrium

    _____ Aorta   _____ Aortic semilunar valve

46.   Word Find

Find and circle 12 terms presented in this chapter. Words may be spelled top to bottom, bottom to top, right to left, left to right, or diagonally.

```
P W S T L W G V F V W Q U S Y
U T X U L Q L V M J W O U J D
R E S P E B S W Z W K N X Q Y
K V Y T E V E N T R I C L E S
I F K U O E L O T S Y S X V R
N G Z O A R G A Y C M X F K H
J B B C U J T R V K P Y P W Y
E V L A V R A N U L I M E S T
F D T I Z N H I Y A A D U T H
I T B D O D S H Y P U R W I M
B P E R I C A R D I U M T D I
E M O A B R A D Y C A R D I A
R C U C E N D O C A R D I U M
S A I D R A C Y H C A T B Y P
```

Bradycardia	Endocardium	Semilunar valve
Cardiac output	Mitral valve	Systole
Coronary sinus	Pericardium	Tachycardia
Dysrhythmia	Purkinje fibers	Ventricle

DID YOU KNOW?

Your heart pumps more than 5 quarts of blood every minute—that's 2,000 gallons a day!

HEART AND HEART DISEASE

Fill in the crossword puzzle.

ACROSS

1. Inflammation of the pericardium
3. A condition in which muscle fibers contract out of step with each other
6. Disease of the myocardial tissue
8. Also known as the *visceral pericardium*
9. Relaxation of the heart
10. Upper chambers of the heart

DOWN

2. Heart specialist
4. Also known as the *sinoatrial node*
5. Complex that occurs as a result of depolarization of the ventricles
7. Also known as the *mitral valve*
8. Graphic record of the heart's electrical activity

CHECK YOUR KNOWLEDGE

Multiple Choice

Circle the correct answer.

1. The superior vena cava carries blood to the:
   A. Left ventricle
   B. Coronary arteries
   C. Right atrium
   D. Pulmonary veins

2. Which of the following events, if any, does *not* precede ventricular contraction?
   A. P wave
   B. Atrial depolarization
   C. Ventricular depolarization
   D. All of these events precede contraction.

3. Which of the following pairs is mismatched?
   A. Angina pectoris—chest pain
   B. Congestive heart failure—left-sided heart failure
   C. Tachycardia—slow heart rhythm
   D. Dysrhythmia—heart block

4. Which of the following statements is *not* true regarding pericarditis?
   A. It may be caused by infection or trauma.
   B. It often causes severe chest pain.
   C. It may result in impairment of the pumping action of the heart.
   D. All of the above statements are true.

5. The outside covering that surrounds and protects the heart is called the:
   A. Endocardium
   B. Myocardium
   C. Pericardium
   D. Ectocardium

6. Thin-walled upper heart cavities that receive blood from veins are called:
   A. Chordae tendineae
   B. Atria
   C. Pericardia
   D. Ventricles

7. A valve that permits blood to flow from the right ventricle into the pulmonary artery is called:
   A. Tricuspid
   B. Mitral
   C. Aortic semilunar
   D. Pulmonary semilunar

8. Ventricular contraction of the heart occurs *immediately after* depolarization of the:
   A. Purkinje fibers
   B. Atrioventricular node
   C. Sinoatrial node
   D. Bundle of His

9. A variation in heart rate during the breathing cycle is called:
   A. Mitral valve prolapse
   B. Fibrillation
   C. Sinus dysrhythmia
   D. None of the above

10. Heart implants:
    A. Allow patients to move around freely without external pumps.
    B. Are artificial hearts that are made of biologically inert synthetic materials.
    C. Weigh approximately 2 pounds.
    D. All of the above are true.

Matching

Match each term in column A with its corresponding term in column B. (Only one answer is correct for each.)

Column A

_____ 11. Heart attack

_____ 12. QRS complex

_____ 13. Systole

_____ 14. Pulmonary circulation

_____ 15. Bicuspid

_____ 16. Heart compression

_____ 17. Heart muscle

_____ 18. Pacemaker

_____ 19. T wave

_____ 20. Chest pain

Column B

A. Sinoatrial node

B. Cardiac tamponade

C. Myocardium

D. Ventricular repolarization

E. Angina pectoris

F. Myocardial infarction

G. Ventricular depolarization

H. Ventricular contraction

I. Lungs

J. Mitral

THE HEART

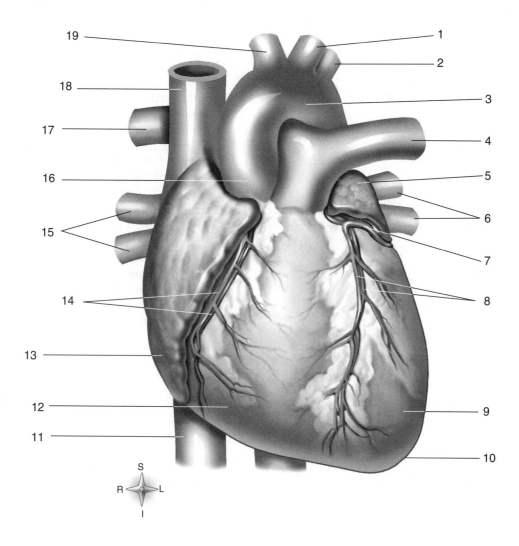

1. _____

2. _____

3. _____

4. _____

5. _____

6. _____

7. _____

8. _____

9. _____

10. _____

11. _____

12. _____

13. _____

14. _____

15. _____

16. _____

17. _____

18. _____

19. _____

CONDUCTION SYSTEM OF THE HEART

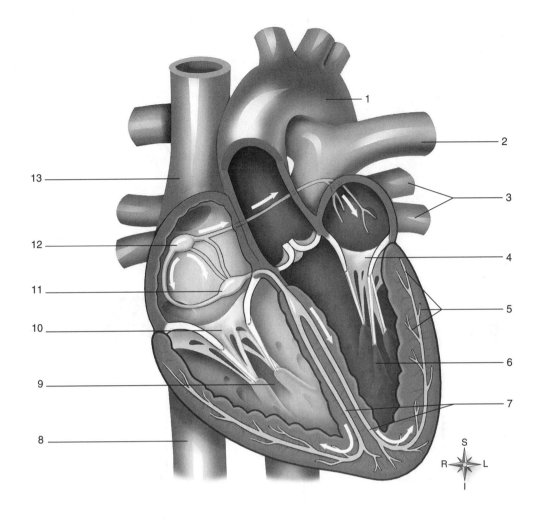

1. _____

2. _____

3. _____

4. _____

5. _____

6. _____

7. _____

8. _____

9. _____

10. _____

11. _____

12. _____

13. _____

NORMAL ECG DEFLECTIONS

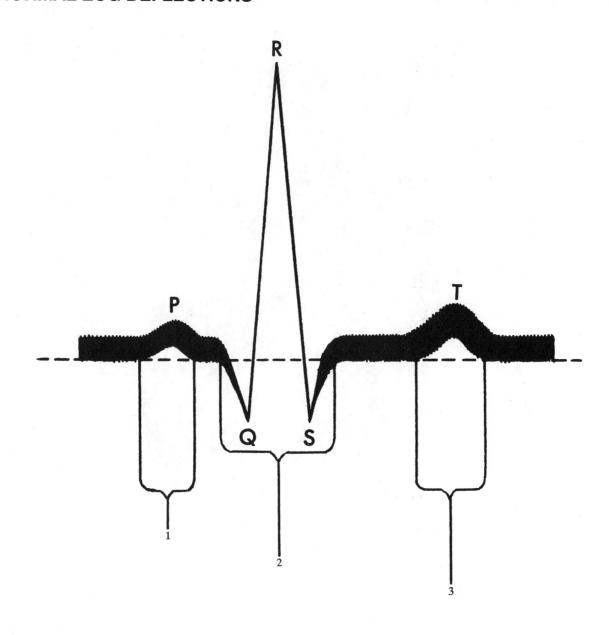

1. _____   3. _____

2. _____

CHAPTER 14

The Circulation of the Blood

One hundred thousand miles of blood vessels make up the elaborate transportation system that circulates materials needed for energy, growth and repair, and also eliminates wastes from your body. These vessels, called *arteries, veins,* and *capillaries,* serve different functions. Arteries carry blood from the heart, veins carry blood to the heart, and capillaries are exchange vessels, or connecting links, between the arteries and veins. The pumping action of the heart keeps blood moving, or circulating, through this closed system of vessels. This system provides distribution of blood to the entire body (systemic circulation) and to specific regions such as the pulmonary circulation or hepatic portal circulation.

Blood pressure is the force of blood in the vessels. This force is highest in the arteries and lowest in the veins. Normal blood pressure varies among individuals and depends on the volume of blood in the arteries. The larger the volume of blood in the arteries, the more pressure is exerted on the walls of the arteries, and the higher the arterial pressure. Conversely, the less blood in the arteries, the lower the blood pressure.

A functional cardiovascular system is vital for survival because without circulation, tissues would lack a supply of oxygen and nutrients. Waste products would begin to accumulate and could become toxic. Your review of this system will provide you with an understanding of the complex transportation mechanism of the body necessary for survival.

TOPICS FOR REVIEW

Before progressing to Chapter 15, you should have an understanding of the structure and function of the blood vessels. Your review should include a study of systemic, pulmonary, hepatic portal, and fetal circulation and should conclude with a thorough understanding of blood pressure, pulse, and circulatory shock.

BLOOD VESSELS

Match each term on the left with its corresponding description on the right.

_____	1. Arteries	A.	Smooth muscle cells that guard the entrance to capillaries
_____	2. Veins	B.	Carry blood to the heart
_____	3. Capillaries	C.	Carry blood into the venules
_____	4. Tunica externa	D.	Carry blood away from the heart
_____	5. Precapillary sphincters	E.	Largest vein
_____	6. Superior vena cava	F.	Largest artery
_____	7. Aorta	G.	Outermost layer of arteries and veins

▶ *If you had difficulty with this section, review pages 395-400.*

DISORDERS OF BLOOD VESSELS

Match each definition on the left with its corresponding term on the right.

_____ 8.   Hardening of the arteries

_____ 9.   Decreased blood supply to a tissue

_____ 10. Tissue death

_____ 11. Necrosis that has progressed to decay

_____ 12. A type of arteriosclerosis caused by lipids

_____ 13. A section of an artery that has become abnormally widened

_____ 14. Varicose veins in the rectum

_____ 15. Vein inflammation

_____ 16. Clot formation

_____ 17. Cerebral vascular accident

A.   Atherosclerosis

B.   Ischemia

C.   Aneurysm

D.   Necrosis

E.   Gangrene

F.   Hemorrhoids

G.   Phlebitis

H.   Stroke

I.   Arteriosclerosis

J.   Thrombus

▶ *If you had difficulty with this section, review pages 400-402.*

CIRCULATION OF BLOOD

Circle the correct answer.

18. The aorta carries blood out of the:
    A. Right atrium
    B. Left atrium
    C. Right ventricle
    D. Left ventricle
    E. None of the above

19. The superior vena cava returns blood to the:
    A. Left atrium
    B. Left ventricle
    C. Right atrium
    D. Right ventricle
    E. None of the above

20. The _____ function as exchange vessels.
    A. Venules
    B. Capillaries
    C. Arteries
    D. Arterioles
    E. Veins

21. Blood returns from the lungs during pulmonary circulation via the:
    A. Pulmonary artery
    B. Pulmonary veins
    C. Aorta
    D. Inferior vena cava

22. The hepatic portal circulation serves the body by:
    A. Removing excess glucose and storing it in the liver as glycogen
    B. Detoxifying blood
    C. Assisting the body to maintain proper blood glucose balance
    D. All of the above

23. The structure used to bypass the liver in the fetal circulation is the:
    A. Foramen ovale
    B. Ductus venosus
    C. Ductus arteriosus
    D. Umbilical vein

24. The foramen ovale serves the fetal circulation by:
    A. Connecting the aorta and the pulmonary artery
    B. Shunting blood from the right atrium directly into the left atrium
    C. Bypassing the liver
    D. Bypassing the lungs

25. The structure used to connect the aorta and pulmonary artery in the fetal circulation is the:
    A. Ductus arteriosus
    B. Ductus venosus
    C. Aorta
    D. Foramen ovale

26. Which of the following is *not* an artery?
    A. Femoral
    B. Popliteal
    C. Coronary
    D. Inferior vena cava

 If you had difficulty with this section, review pages 402-406.

BLOOD PRESSURE

PULSE

If the statement is true, write "T" in the answer blank. If the statement is false, correct the statement by circling the incorrect term and writing the correct term in the answer blank.

_____ 27. Blood pressure is highest in the veins and lowest in the arteries.

_____ 28. The difference between two blood pressures is referred to as *blood pressure deficit.*

_____ 29. If the blood pressure in the arteries were to decrease so that it became equal to the average pressure in the arterioles, circulation would increase.

_____ 30. A stroke is often the result of low blood pressure.

_____ 31. Massive hemorrhage increases blood pressure.

_____ 32. Blood pressure is the volume of blood in the vessels.

_____ 33. Both the strength and the rate of heartbeat affect cardiac output and blood pressure.

_____ 34. The diameter of the arterioles helps determine how much blood drains out of arteries into arterioles.

_____ 35. A stronger heartbeat tends to decrease blood pressure and a weaker heartbeat tends to increase it.

_____ 36. The systolic pressure is the pressure being exerted against the vessels while the ventricles relax.

_____ 37. If blood becomes less viscous than normal, blood pressure increases.

_____ 38. A device called a *sphygmomanometer* is used to measure blood pressures in clinical situations.

_____ 39. Loud, tapping Korotkoff sounds suddenly begin when the cuff pressure measured by the mercury column equals the systolic pressure.

_____ 40. The venous blood pressure within the left atrium is called the *central venous pressure.*

_____ 41. The pulse is a vein expanding and then recoiling.

_____ 42. The radial artery is located at the wrist.

_____ 43. The common carotid artery is located in the neck along the front edge of the sternocleidomastoid muscle.

_____ 44. The artery located at the bend of the elbow that is used for locating the pulse is the dorsalis pedis.

 If you had difficulty with this section, review pages 406-413.

CIRCULATORY SHOCK

Fill in the blanks.

45. Complications of septicemia may result in _____
_____.

46. _____ _____ results from any type
of heart failure.

47. An acute type of allergic reaction called _____ results in
_____ _____.

48. _____ _____ results from wide-
spread dilation of blood vessels caused by an imbalance in autonomic stimulation of smooth muscles in
vessel walls.

49. *Hypovolemia* means "_____ _____
_____."

50. A type of septic shock that results from staphylococcal infections that begin in the vagina of menstruating
women and spread to the blood is _____
_____ _____.

▶ *If you had difficulty with this section, review pages 413-415.*

UNSCRAMBLE THE WORDS

51. **S T M E S Y C I**

☐◯☐◯☐☐☐☐

52. **N U L V E E**

◯☐☐☐☐◯

53. **R Y T R E A**

☐☐☐◯☐☐

54. **U S L E P**

☐☐◯☐☐

Take the circled letters, unscramble them, and fill in the solution.

How Noah survived the flood.

55. ☐☐☐☐☐☐☐

APPLYING WHAT YOU KNOW

56. Caryl was enjoying a picnic lunch one day when a bee suddenly flew down and stung her. Within seconds, Caryl began to experience difficulty breathing, tachycardia, a decrease in blood pressure, and cyanosis. What is Caryl experiencing?

57. Wilson was scheduled to undergo extensive surgery. His surgeon, Dr. Berger, requested that two units of blood be available for Wilson should he require them. What complication of surgery was Dr. Berger hoping to avoid?

58. Rochelle is a hairstylist who works long hours. Lately she has noticed that her feet are sore and edematous. What might be the cause of these symptoms? What advice could offer Rochelle some relief from these symptoms?

59. Rubin returned from surgery in stable condition. The nurse noted that each time she took Rubin's pulse and blood pressure, the pulse became higher and the blood pressure lower than the last time. What might be the cause?

60. Word Find

Find and circle 15 terms presented in this chapter. Words may be spelled top to bottom, bottom to top, right to left, left to right, or diagonally.

```
Y H Y S I S O B M O R H T A R
L A C I L I B M U O A Y N I Y
E E S Y S T E M I C C G D E U
M V E N U L E D D C I X M D I
E Y M U I R T A R N L E C G Y
N O I T A Z I R A L O P E D N
U D L A T R O P C I T A P E H
S I U K M U E T O E S L U P U
R P N F Y C B E D R A L Z P J
D S A H T I T V N L I I B D W
Q U R O I V A Q E O D A K R K
K C R M P G A I G N D D Z Y J
Y I Y R I N E A F Z L Q S P X
S R M I C C Q O A W U N H O K
P T A V H H Z L H I J J X K Z
```

Angina pectoris	ECG	Systemic
Apex	Endocardium	Thrombosis
Atrium	Hepatic portal	Tricuspid
Depolarization	Pulse	Umbilical
Diastolic	Semilunar	Venule

DID YOU KNOW?

Every pound of excess fat contains 200 miles of additional capillaries.

If laid out in a straight line, the average adult's circulatory system would be nearly 60,000 miles long—enough to circle the earth 2.5 times!

CIRCULATION OF THE BLOOD

Fill in the crossword puzzle.

ACROSS

2. Inflammation of the lining of the heart
3. Bicuspid valve (two words)
5. Inner layer of pericardium
7. Cardiopulmonary resuscitation (abbreviation)
10. Carries blood away from the heart
11. Upper chamber of heart
12. Lower chambers of the heart
13. SA node

DOWN

1. Unique blood circulation through the liver (two words)
3. Muscular layer of the heart
4. Carries blood to the heart
6. Tiny artery
8. Heart rate
9. Carries blood from arterioles into venules

CHECK YOUR KNOWLEDGE

Multiple Choice

Circle the correct answer.

1. The medical term for high blood pressure is:
    A. Arteriosclerosis
    B. Cyanosis
    C. Hypertension
    D. Central venous pressure

2. Septic shock is caused by:
    A. Complications of toxins in the blood
    B. A nerve condition
    C. A drop in blood pressure
    D. Blood vessel dilation

3. Hypovolemic shock is caused by:
    A. Heart failure
    B. Dilated blood vessels
    C. A drop in blood volume
    D. A severe allergic reaction

4. Which vessels collect blood from the capillaries and return it to the heart?
    A. Arteries
    B. Sinuses
    C. Veins
    D. Arterioles

5. The innermost coat of an artery that comes into direct contact with blood is called the:
    A. Lumen
    B. Tunica externa
    C. Tunica intima
    D. Tunica media

6. Hemorrhoids can best be described as:
    A. Varicose veins
    B. Varicose veins in the rectum
    C. Thrombophlebitis of the rectum
    D. Clot formation in the rectum

7. In the fetal circulation:
    A. The ductus venosus allows most blood from the placenta to bypass the fetal liver.
    B. The umbilical vein carries oxygen-poor blood.
    C. The foramen ovale connects the aorta and the pulmonary artery.
    D. None of the above are true.

8. Which of the following events, if any, would *not* cause the blood pressure to increase?
    A. Hemorrhaging
    B. Increasing the viscosity of the blood
    C. Increasing the strength of the heartbeat
    D. All of the above

9. Arteriosclerosis is a disorder of the:
    A. Heart
    B. Veins
    C. Capillaries
    D. Arteries

10. A common type of vascular disease that occludes arteries by lipids and other matter is:
    A. Arteriosclerotic plaque
    B. Atherosclerosis
    C. Varicose veins
    D. Thrombophlebitis

Matching

Match each description in column A with its corresponding term in column B. (There is only one correct answer for each item.)

Column A

_____ 11. Largest artery

_____ 12. Decreased blood supply

_____ 13. Leg vein

_____ 14. Fetal circulation

_____ 15. Arterial procedure

_____ 16. Vein inflammation

_____ 17. Lung circulation

_____ 18. Weakened artery

_____ 19. Largest vein

_____ 20. Myocardial infarction

Column B

A.   Ischemia

B.   Phlebitis

C.   Foramen ovale

D.   Aneurysm

E.   Vena cava

F.   Angioplasty

G.   Aorta

H.   Pulmonary

I.   Great saphenous vein

J.   Cardiogenic shock

FETAL CIRCULATION

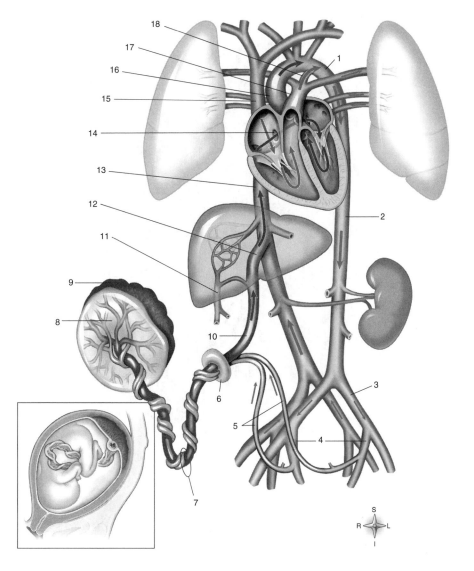

1. _____

2. _____

3. _____

4. _____

5. _____

6. _____

7. _____

8. _____

9. _____

10. _____

11. _____

12. _____

13. _____

14. _____

15. _____

16. _____

17. _____

18. _____

HEPATIC PORTAL CIRCULATION

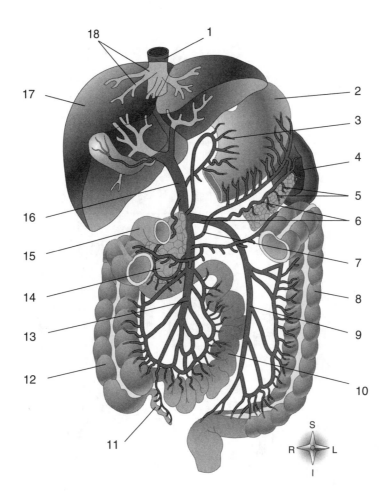

1. _____

2. _____

3. _____

4. _____

5. _____

6. _____

7. _____

8. _____

9. _____

10. _____

11. _____

12. _____

13. _____

14. _____

15. _____

16. _____

17. _____

18. _____

PRINCIPAL ARTERIES OF THE BODY

1. _____
2. _____
3. _____
4. _____
5. _____
6. _____
7. _____
8. _____
9. _____
10. _____
11. _____
12. _____
13. _____
14. _____
15. _____
16. _____
17. _____
18. _____
19. _____
20. _____
21. _____
22. _____
23. _____
24. _____
25. _____
26. _____
27. _____
28. _____
29. _____
30. _____

PRINCIPAL VEINS OF THE BODY

1. _____
2. _____
3. _____
4. _____
5. _____
6. _____
7. _____
8. _____
9. _____
10. _____
11. _____
12. _____
13. _____
14. _____
15. _____
16. _____
17. _____
18. _____
19. _____
20. _____
21. _____
22. _____
23. _____
24. _____
25. _____
26. _____
27. _____
28. _____
29. _____
30. _____
31. _____
32. _____
33. _____
34. _____
35. _____
36. _____
37. _____
38. _____

CHAPTER 15

The Lymphatic System and Immunity

The lymphatic system is similar to the circulatory system. Lymph, like blood, flows through an elaborate route of vessels. In addition to lymphatic vessels, the lymphatic system consists of lymph nodes, lymph, the thymus, tonsils, and the spleen. Unlike the circulatory system, the lymphatic vessels do not form a closed circuit. Lymph flows only once through the vessels before draining into the general blood circulation. This system is a filtering mechanism for microorganisms and serves as a protective device against foreign invaders such as cancer.

The immune system is the armed forces division of the body. Ready to attack at a moment's notice, the immune system defends us against the major enemies of the body: microorganisms, foreign transplanted tissue cells, and our own cells that have turned malignant.

The most numerous cells of the immune system are the lymphocytes. These cells circulate in the body's fluids seeking invading organisms and destroying them with powerful lymphotoxins, lymphokines, or antibodies.

Phagocytes, another large group of immune system cells, assist with the destruction of foreign invaders by a process known as *phagocytosis*. Neutrophils, monocytes, and connective tissue cells called *macrophages* use this process to surround unwanted microorganisms and ingest and digest them, rendering them harmless to the body.

Another weapon that the immune system possesses is complement. Normally a group of inactive enzymes present in the blood, complement can be activated to kill invading cells by drilling holes in their cytoplasmic membranes, which allows fluid to enter the cell until it bursts.

Your review of this chapter will give you an understanding of how the body defends itself from the daily invasion of destructive substances.

TOPICS FOR REVIEW

Before progressing to Chapter 16, you should familiarize yourself with the functions of the lymphatic system, the immune system, and the major structures that make up these systems. Your review should include knowledge of lymphatic vessels, lymph nodes, lymph, lymphatic organs and tissues, antibodies, complement, and the development of B and T cells. Your study should also include the differences in humoral and cell-mediated immunity. Finally, an understanding of the excessive responses of the immune system and immune system deficiencies are necessary to complete your review of this chapter.

THE LYMPHATIC SYSTEM

Fill in the blanks.

1. _____ is a specialized fluid formed in the tissue spaces that will be transported by way of specialized vessels to eventually reenter the circulatory system.

2. Blood plasma that has filtered out of capillaries into microscopic spaces between cells is called _____ _____.

3. Tiny blind-ended tubes distributed in the tissue spaces are called _____ _____.

4. Lymph eventually empties into two terminal vessels called the _____ _____ _____ and the _____ _____.

5. The thoracic duct has an enlarged pouchlike structure called the _____ _____.

6. Lymph is filtered by moving through _____ _____, which are located in clusters along the pathway of lymphatic vessels.

7. Lymph enters the node through four _____ lymph vessels.

8. Lymph exits the node through a single _____ lymph vessel.

9. An abnormal condition in which tissues exhibit edema because of the accumulation of lymph is _____.

10. Hodgkin disease is an example of _____.

▶ *If you had difficulty with this section, review pages 421-427.*

THYMUS
TONSILS
SPLEEN

Match each numbered description to one of the lymphatic system structures. Write the corresponding letter in the answer blank.

A. Thymus   B. Tonsils   C. Spleen

_____ 11. Palatine, pharyngeal, and lingual are examples

_____ 12. The largest lymphoid organ in the body

_____ 13. Destroys worn-out red blood cells

_____ 14. Located in the mediastinum

_____ 15. Serves as a reservoir for blood

_____ 16. T-lymphocytes

_____ 17. Largest at puberty

▶ *If you had difficulty with this section, review pages 427-428.*

THE IMMUNE SYSTEM

Match each term on the left with its corresponding description on the right.

_____ 18.   Nonspecific immunity   A.   Innate immunity

_____ 19.   Phagocytes   B.   Acquired immunity

_____ 20.   Specific immunity   C.   General protection

_____ 21.   Lymphocytes   D.   Artificial exposure

_____ 22.   Immunization   E.   Memory

IMMUNE SYSTEM MOLECULES

Match each description with its related term. Write the corresponding letter in the answer blank.

_____ 23.   A type of very specific antibodies produced from a   A.   Antibodies
             population of identical cells

_____ 24.   Protein compounds normally present in the body   B.   Antigen

_____ 25.   Also known as *antibody-mediated immunity*   C.   Monoclonal

_____ 26.   Combines with antibody to produce humoral immunity   D.   Complement cascade

_____ 27.   Antibody   E.   Complement

_____ 28.   The process of changing antibody molecule shape   F.   Humoral
             slightly to expose binding sites

_____ 29.   Capable of producing large quantities of very specific   G.   Combining site
             antibodies

_____ 30.   Inactive proteins in blood   H.   Hybridomas

▶ *If you had difficulty with this section, review pages 428-433.*

IMMUNE SYSTEM CELLS

Circle the correct answer.

31. The most numerous cells of the immune system
    are the:
    A. Monocytes
    B. Eosinophils
    C. Neutrophils
    D. Lymphocytes
    E. Complement

32. The second stage of B cell development changes
    a mature inactive B cell into a/an:
    A. Plasma cell
    B. Stem cell
    C. Antibody
    D. Activated B cell
    E. Immature B cell

33. Which one of the following is activated last in
    the immune process?
    A. Plasma cells
    B. Stem cells
    C. Antibodies
    D. Activated B cells
    E. Immature B cells

34. Which one of the following is part of the cell
    membrane of B cells?
    A. Complement
    B. Antigens
    C. Antibodies
    D. Epitopes
    E. None of the above

35. Immature B cells have:
    A. Four types of defense mechanisms on their cell membrane
    B. Several kinds of defense mechanisms on their cell membrane
    C. One specific kind of defense mechanism on their cell membrane
    D. No defense mechanisms on their cell membrane

36. Development of an active B cell depends on the B cell coming in contact with:
    A. Complement
    B. Antibodies
    C. Lymphotoxins
    D. Lymphokines
    E. Antigens

37. The kind of cell that produces large numbers of antibodies is the:
    A. B cell
    B. Stem cell
    C. T cell
    D. Memory cell
    E. Plasma cell

38. Just one of these short-lived cells that make antibodies can produce _____ of them per second.
    A. 20
    B. 200
    C. 2,000
    D. 20,000

39. Which of the following statements is *not* true of memory cells?
    A. They can secrete antibodies.
    B. They are found in lymph nodes.
    C. They develop into plasma cells.
    D. They can react with antigens.
    E. All of the above are true of memory cells.

40. T cell development begins in the:
    A. Lymph nodes
    B. Liver
    C. Pancreas
    D. Spleen
    E. Thymus

41. B cells function indirectly to produce:
    A. Humoral immunity
    B. Cell-mediated immunity
    C. Lymphotoxins
    D. Lymphokines

42. T cells function to produce:
    A. Humoral immunity
    B. Cell-mediated immunity
    C. Antibodies
    D. Memory cells

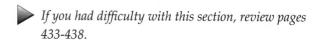 *If you had difficulty with this section, review pages 433-438.*

HYPERSENSITIVITY OF THE IMMUNE SYSTEM

Circle the correct answer.

43. The term *allergy* is used to describe (*hypersensitivity* or *hyposensitivity*) of the immune system to relatively harmless environmental antigens.

44. Antigens that trigger an allergic response are often called (*antibodies* or *allergens*).

45. (*Anaphylactic shock* or *Urticaria*) is a life-threatening condition.

46. A common autoimmune disease is (*lupus* or *SCID*).

47. Erythroblastosis fetalis is an example of (*isoimmunity* or *autoimmunity*).

48. The antigens most commonly involved in transplant rejection are called (*SCIDs* or *HLAs*).

If you had difficulty with this section, review 438-441.

IMMUNE DEFICIENCY

Match each condition with its origin. Write the corresponding letter in the answer blank.

A. Congenital   B. Acquired (after birth)

_____ 49. AIDS

_____ 50. SCID

_____ 51. Improper B cell development

_____ 52. Viral infection

_____ 53. Genetic defect

▶ *If you had difficulty with this section, review pages 441-442.*

UNSCRAMBLE THE WORDS

54. **N T C M P E O L E M**

55. **M T M Y I U N I**

56. **O E N C L S**

57. **F N R O E R T E N I**

Take the circled letters, unscramble them, and fill in the solution.

What the student was praying for the night before exams.

58.

...and please, don't let me forget to remember!

APPLYING WHAT YOU KNOW

59. Two-year old baby Metcalfe was exposed to chickenpox and subsequently developed the disease. What type of immunity will be developed as a result of this?

60. Marcia was a bisexual and an intravenous drug user. She has developed a type of skin cancer known as Kaposi sarcoma. What is Marcia's primary diagnosis?

61. Baby Wilson was born without a thymus gland. Immediate plans were made for a transplant to be performed. In the meantime, baby Wilson was placed in strict isolation. For what reason was he placed in isolation?

62. Word Find

Find and circle 14 terms presented in this chapter. Words may be spelled top to bottom, bottom to top, right to left, left to right, or diagonally.

```
I  N  F  L  A  M  M  A  T  O  R  Y  F  C  G
Q  N  L  O  Y  Z  O  C  C  P  A  O  F  S  X
M  W  T  A  A  M  N  J  X  Q  K  R  N  P  H
U  R  L  E  R  M  P  X  B  R  U  I  A  L  C
C  M  A  C  R  O  P  H  A  G  E  I  E  D  Z
X  M  N  D  K  F  M  N  O  T  U  C  R  N  M
A  E  O  R  E  Z  E  U  O  C  F  B  Y  E  B
Y  P  L  E  B  G  G  R  H  T  Y  T  S  E  D
Y  S  C  R  I  S  P  J  O  E  I  T  M  L  A
Z  M  O  T  J  X  E  T  O  N  A  E  E  P  X
T  O  N  S  I  L  S  S  U  M  Y  H  T  S  Y
W  A  O  C  J  N  I  M  W  K  O  Z  E  N  D
D  W  M  K  W  R  M  O  I  P  S  H  Y  B  G
F  H  W  U  J  I  Z  F  V  D  Z  L  Y  T  X
```

Acquired	Interferon	Proteins
Antigen	Lymph	Spleen
Humoral	Lymphocytes	Thymus
Immunity	Macrophage	Tonsils
Inflammatory	Monoclonal	

DID YOU KNOW?

In the United States, the HIV infection rate is increasing four times faster in women than in men. Women tend to underestimate their risk.

Ten percent of all HIV/AIDS cases are individuals 50 years of age and older.

LYMPH AND IMMUNITY

Fill in the crossword puzzle.

ACROSS

1. Largest lymphoid organ in the body
3. Connective tissue cells that are phagocytes
4. Protein compounds normally present in the body
5. Remain in reserve then turn into plasma cells when needed (two words)
9. Synthetically produced to fight certain diseases
10. Lymph exits the node through this lymph vessel

11. Lymph enters the node through these lymph vessels

DOWN

2. Secretes a copious amount of antibodies into the blood (two words)
6. Inactive proteins
7. Family of identical cells descended from one cell
8. Type of lymphocyte (humoral immunity—two words)
11. Immune deficiency disorder

12. Type of lymphocyte (cell-mediated immunity—two words)

CHECK YOUR KNOWLEDGE

Multiple Choice

Circle the correct answer.

1. T cells do which of the following?
   A. Develop in the thymus
   B. Form memory cells
   C. Form plasma cells
   D. All of the above

2. Lymph does which of the following?
   A. Forms as blood plasma filters out of capillaries
   B. Empties into the heart
   C. Flows through lymphatic arteries
   D. All of the above

3. Acquired immune deficiency syndrome is characterized by which of the following?
   A. Caused by a retrovirus
   B. Causes inadequate T cell formation
   C. Can result in death from cancer or infection
   D. All of the above

4. Interferon is:
   A. Produced by B cells
   B. A protein compound that protects other cells by interfering with the ability of a virus to reproduce
   C. A group of inactive enzyme proteins normally present in blood
   D. All of the above

5. B cells do which of the following?
   A. Develop into plasma cells and memory cells
   B. Establish humoral immunity
   C. Develop from primitive cells in bone marrow called *stem cells*
   D. All of the above

6. Which of the following functions to kill invading cells by drilling a hole in the plasma membrane?
   A. Interferon
   B. Complement cascade
   C. Antibody
   D. Memory cell

7. Which of the following cell types function in the immune system?
   A. Macrophages
   B. Lymphocytes
   C. T cells
   D. All of the above

8. Which of the following is an example of phagocytes?
   A. Dendritic cells
   B. Neutrophils
   C. Macrophages
   D. All of the above

9. What is a rapidly growing population of identical cells that produce large quantities of specific antibodies called?
   A. Complementary
   B. Lymphotoxic
   C. Chemotactic
   D. Monoclonal

10. Which of the following is a form of passive natural immunity?
    A. A child develops measles and acquires an immunity to subsequent infection.
    B. Antibodies are injected into an infected individual.
    C. An infant receives protection through its mother's milk.
    D. Vaccinations are given against smallpox.

Matching

Match each of the terms in column A with its corresponding description in column B. (Only one answer is correct for each.)

Column A

_____ 11. Adenoids

_____ 12. B cell

_____ 13. Clone

_____ 14. HIV virus

_____ 15. Complement

_____ 16. Filtration

_____ 17. Cisterna chyli

_____ 18. T cell

_____ 19. Vaccination

_____ 20. Antigen

Column B

A. Thoracic duct

B. Lymph node

C. Artificial immunity

D. Humoral immunity

E. Pharyngeal tonsils

F. Shaped to combine with an antibody

G. Inactive proteins

H. AIDS

I. Identical cells

J. Cell-mediated immunity

PRINCIPAL ORGANS OF THE LYMPHATIC SYSTEM

1. _____

2. _____

3. _____

4. _____

5. _____

6. _____

7. _____

8. _____

9. _____

10. _____

11. _____

12. _____

13. _____

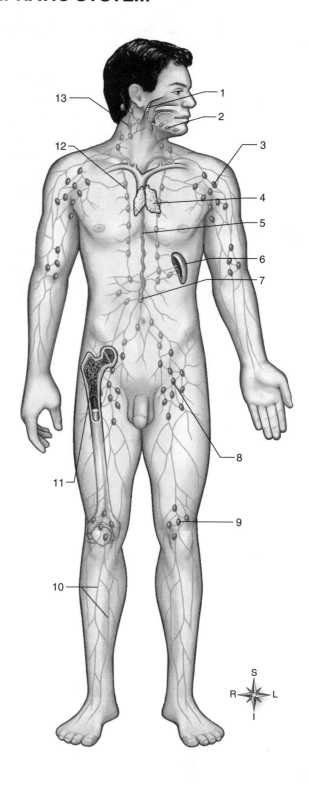

CHAPTER 16

The Respiratory System

As you sit reviewing this system, your body needs 16 quarts of air per minute. Walking requires 24 quarts of air, and running requires 50 quarts per minute. The respiratory system provides the air necessary for you to perform your daily activities and eliminates the waste gases from the air that you breathe. Take a deep breath, and think of the air as entering some 250 million tiny air sacs similar in appearance to clusters of grapes. These microscopic air sacs expand to let air in and contract to force it out. These tiny sacs, or alveoli, are the functioning units of the respiratory system. They provide the necessary volume of oxygen and eliminate carbon dioxide 24 hours a day.

Air enters either through the mouth or the nasal cavity. It next passes through the pharynx and past the epiglottis, through the glottis and the rest of the larynx. It then continues down the trachea, into the bronchi to the bronchioles, and finally through the alveoli. The reverse occurs for expelled air.

The exchange of gases between air in the lungs and in the blood is known as *external respiration*. The exchange of gases that occurs between the blood and the cells of the body is known as *internal respiration*. By constantly supplying adequate oxygen and removing carbon dioxide as it forms, the respiratory system helps maintain an environment conducive to maximum cell efficiency.

Your review of this system is necessary to provide you with an understanding of this essential homeostatic mechanism that supplies oxygen to our cells.

TOPICS FOR REVIEW

Before progressing to Chapter 17, you should have an understanding of the structure and function of the organs of the respiratory system. Your review should include knowledge of the mechanisms responsible for both internal and external respiration. Your study should conclude with a knowledge of the volumes of air exchanged in pulmonary ventilation, an understanding of how respiration is regulated, and the common disorders of the respiratory tract.

STRUCTURAL PLAN
RESPIRATORY TRACTS
RESPIRATORY MUCOSA

Match each term with its definition. Write the corresponding letter in the answer blank.

_____ 1.   Function of respiratory system
_____ 2.   Pharynx
_____ 3.   Passive transport process responsible for
            actual exchange of gases
_____ 4.   Assists with the movement of mucus toward
            the pharynx
_____ 5.   Barrier between the blood in the capillaries
            and the air in the alveolus
_____ 6.   Lines the tubes of the respiratory tree
_____ 7.   Terminal air sacs
_____ 8.   Trachea
_____ 9.   Surround alveoli
_____ 10. Homeostatic mechanism

A. Diffusion
B. Respiratory membrane
C. Alveoli

D. Capillaries

E. Respiration

F. Respiratory mucosa
G. Upper respiratory tract
H. Lower respiratory tract
I. Cilia
J. Air distributor

Fill in the blanks.

The organs of the respiratory system are designed to perform two basic functions. They serve as an

(11) _____ _____ and as a

(12) _____ _____. In addition to the

functions given above, the respiratory system (13) _____,

(14) _____, and (15) _____ the air we

breathe. Respiratory organs include the (16) _____,

(17) _____, (18) _____,

(19) _____, (20) _____, and the

(21) _____. The respiratory system ends in millions of tiny, thin-walled sacs

called (22) _____. (23) _____ of gases

takes place in these sacs. Two aspects of the structure of these sacs assist them in the exchange of gases. First,

an extremely thin membrane, the (24) _____

_____, allows for easy exchange, and second, the large number of air sacs

makes an enormous (25) _____ area.

▶ *If you had difficulty with this section, review pages 453-457.*

NOSE
PHARYNX
LARYNX
DISORDERS OF UPPER RESPIRATORY TRACT

Circle the term in each word group that does not belong.

26. Nares   Septum   Oropharynx   Conchae

27. Conchae   Frontal   Maxillary   Sphenoidal

28. Oropharynx   Throat   5 inches   Epiglottis

29. Pharyngeal   Adenoids   Uvula   Nasopharynx

30. Middle ear   Tubes   Nasopharynx   Larynx

31. Voice box   Thyroid cartilage Tonsils   Vocal cords

32. Palatine   Eustachian tube   Tonsils   Oropharynx

33. Pharynx   Epiglottis   Adam's apple   Voice box

Match each numbered term or phrase with the corresponding respiratory structure.

A. Nose   B. Pharynx   C. Larynx

_____ 34. Warms and humidifies air

_____ 35. Air and food pass through here

_____ 36. Sinuses

_____ 37. Conchae

_____ 38. Septum

_____ 39. Tonsils

_____ 40. Middle ear infections

_____ 41. Epiglottis

_____ 42. Rhinitis

_____ 43. Sore throat

_____ 44. Epistaxis

▶ *If you had difficulty with this section, review pages 457-463.*

TRACHEA
BRONCHI, BRONCHIOLES, AND ALVEOLI
LUNGS AND PLEURA

Fill in the blanks.

45. The windpipe is more properly referred to as the _____.

46. _____ ensure that the framework of the trachea is almost noncollapsible.

47. A life-saving technique designed to free the trachea of ingested food or foreign objects is the
_____ _____.

48. The first branch or division of the trachea leading to the lungs is the _____
_____.

49. Each alveolar duct ends in several _____
_____.

50. The narrow part of each lung, up under the collarbone, is its _____.

51. The _____ covers the outer surface of the lungs and lines the inner surface of the rib cage.

52. Inflammation of the lining of the thoracic cavity is _____.

53. The presence of air in the pleural space on one side of the chest is a _____.

▶ *If you had difficulty with this section, review pages 463-466.*

RESPIRATION

If the statement is true, write "T" in the answer blank. If the statement is false, correct the statement by circling the incorrect term and writing the correct term in the answer blank.

_____ 54. Diffusion is the process that moves air into and out of the lungs.

_____ 55. For inspiration to take place, the diaphragm and other respiratory muscles must relax.

_____ 56. Diffusion is a passive process that results in movement up a concentration gradient.

_____ 57. The exchange of gases that occurs between blood in tissue capillaries and the body cells is external respiration.

_____ 58. Many different pulmonary volumes can be measured by having a person breathe into a spirometer.

_____ 59. Ordinarily we take about 2 pints of air into our lungs with each breath.

_____ 60. The amount of air normally breathed in and out with each breath is called *tidal volume.*

_____ 61. The largest amount of air that one can breathe out in one expiration is called *residual volume.*

_____ 62. The inspiratory reserve volume is the amount of air that can be forcibly inhaled after a normal inspiration.

▶ *If you had difficulty with this section, review pages 466-472.*

Circle the correct answer.

63. The term that means the same thing as breathing is:
    A. Gas exchange
    B. Respiration
    C. Inspiration
    D. Expiration
    E. Pulmonary ventilation

64. Carbaminohemoglobin is formed when _____ bind(s) to hemoglobin.
    A. Oxygen
    B. Amino acids
    C. Carbon dioxide
    D. Nitrogen
    E. None of the above

65. Most of the oxygen transported by the blood is:
    A. Dissolved into white blood cells
    B. Bound to white blood cells
    C. Bound to hemoglobin
    D. Bound to carbaminohemoglobin
    E. None of the above

66. Which of the following does *not* occur during inspiration?
    A. Elevation of the ribs
    B. Elevation of the diaphragm
    C. Contraction of the diaphragm
    D. Elongation of the chest cavity from top to bottom

67. A young adult male would have a vital capacity of about _____ mL.
    A. 500
    B. 1200
    C. 3300
    D. 4800
    E. 6200

68. The amount of air that can be forcibly exhaled after expiring the tidal volume is known as the:
    A. Total lung capacity
    B. Vital capacity
    C. Inspiratory reserve volume
    D. Expiratory reserve volume
    E. None of the above

69. Which one of the following formulas is correct?
    A. VC = TV - IRV + ERV
    B. VC = TV + IRV - ERV
    C. VC = TV + IRV × ERV
    D. VC = TV + IRV + ERV
    E. None of the above

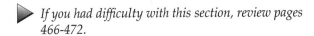 *If you had difficulty with this section, review pages 466-472.*

REGULATION OF RESPIRATION
RECEPTORS INFLUENCING RESPIRATION
TYPES OF BREATHING

Match each term on the left with the corresponding description on the right.

_____ 70. Inspiratory center
_____ 71. Chemoreceptors
_____ 72. Pulmonary stretch receptors
_____ 73. Dyspnea
_____ 74. Respiratory arrest
_____ 75. Eupnea
_____ 76. Hypoventilation

A. Difficult breathing
B. Located in carotid bodies
C. Slow and shallow respirations
D. Normal respiratory rate
E. Located in the medulla
F. Failure to resume breathing after a period of apnea
G. Located throughout pulmonary airways and in the alveoli

If you had difficulty with this section, review pages 472-474.

DISORDERS OF THE LOWER RESPIRATORY TRACT

Fill in the blanks.

77. _____ is an acute inflammation of the lungs in which the alveoli and bronchi become plugged with thick fluid.

78. _____ is still a major cause of death in many poor, densely populated regions of the world. It has recently reemerged as an important health problem in some major U.S. cities.

79. _____ may result from the progression of chronic bronchitis or other conditions as air becomes trapped within alveoli, causing them to enlarge and eventually rupture.

80. _____ is an obstructive disorder characterized by recurring spasms of the smooth muscle in the walls of the bronchial air passages.

▶ *If you had difficulty with this section, review pages 474-479.*

UNSCRAMBLE THE WORDS

81. **S P U E L I R Y**

◯ ▢ ▢ ◯ ▢ ▢ ▢

82. **C R N B O S I T H I**

▢ ▢ ◯ ◯ ▢ ▢ ◯ ▢ ▢ ▢

83. **S E S X P T I A I**

▢ ▢ ▢ ◯ ◯ ▢ ▢ ◯ ▢

84. **D D N E A O I S**

▢ ▢ ▢ ▢ ◯ ▢ ◯ ▢

Take the circled letters, unscramble them, and fill in the solution.

What Mona Lisa was to DaVinci.

85. ▢▢▢▢▢▢▢▢▢▢▢▢▢▢▢

APPLYING WHAT YOU KNOW

86. Mr. Gorski is a heavy smoker. Recently he has noticed that when he gets up in the morning, he has a bothersome cough that brings up a large accumulation of mucus. This cough persists for several minutes and then leaves until the next morning. What is an explanation for this problem?

87. Penny is 5 years old and is a mouth breather. She has had repeated episodes of tonsillitis, and her pediatrician, Dr. Smith, has suggested removal of her tonsils and adenoids. He further suggests that the surgery will probably cure her mouth breathing problem. Why is this a possibility?

88. Sandy developed emphysema. This disease reduces the capacity of the lungs to recoil elastically. Which respiratory air volumes will this condition affect? Why?

89. Word Find

Find and circle 14 terms presented in this chapter. Words may be spelled top to bottom, bottom to top, right to left, left to right, or diagonally.

```
N  K  S  A  Q  B  I  L  V  A  D  T  I  X  D
O  X  O  O  B  F  I  F  G  I  M  N  R  G  Y
I  G  N  X  W  D  E  E  F  L  B  A  U  T  S
T  B  K  Y  N  H  E  F  O  I  U  T  I  R  P
A  T  M  H  E  O  U  T  R  C  C  C  P  V  N
L  L  A  E  P  S  I  R  I  Z  A  A  N  F  E
I  P  T  M  I  H  G  T  I  P  R  F  P  C  A
T  U  B  O  G  Q  E  V  A  Q  O  R  V  N  W
N  L  N  G  L  R  J  C  C  R  T  U  P  D  C
E  M  U  L  O  V  L  A  U  D  I  S  E  R  E
V  O  V  O  T  A  N  G  J  E  D  P  Z  U  U
O  N  K  B  T  C  N  U  U  E  B  O  S  J  S
P  A  L  I  I  K  E  U  C  N  O  Z  K  N  A
Y  R  V  N  S  D  I  O  N  E  D  A  M  F  I
H  Y  O  M  L  O  A  Z  D  T  Y  M  N  L  K
```

Adenoids
Carotid body
Cilia
Diffusion
Dyspnea

Epiglottis
Hypoventilation
Inspiration
Oxyhemoglobin
Pulmonary

Residual volume
Surfactant
URI
Vital capacity

DID YOU KNOW?

If the alveoli in our lungs were flattened out they would cover one-half of a tennis court.

Eighty percent of lung cancer cases are due to cigarette smoking.

RESPIRATORY SYSTEM

Fill in the crossword puzzle.

ACROSS

1. Device used to measure the amount of air exchanged in breathing
6. Expiratory reserve volume (abbreviation)
7. Sphenoidal (two words)
8. Terminal air sacs
9. Shelflike structures that protrude into the nasal cavity
11. Inflammation of pleura
12. Respirations stop

DOWN

2. Surgical procedure to remove tonsils
3. Doctor who developed life-saving technique
4. Windpipe
5. Trachea branches into right and left structures
10. Voice box

CHECK YOUR KNOWLEDGE

Multiple Choice

Circle the correct answer.

1. Chemoreceptors in the carotid and aortic bodies are characterized by which of the following?
   A. Sensitive to increases in blood carbon dioxide level
   B. Found in the brain
   C. Sensitive to increases in blood oxygen level
   D. Send impulses to the heart

2. What is the lowest segment of the pharynx called?
   A. Oropharynx
   B. Laryngopharynx
   C. Nasopharynx
   D. Hypopharynx

3. What is the narrow upper portion of a lung called?
   A. Base
   B. Notch
   C. Costal surface
   D. Apex

4. What is the largest amount of air that a person can breathe in and out in one inspiration and expiration called?
   A. Tidal volume
   B. Vital capacity
   C. Residual volume
   D. Inspiratory reserve volume

5. Which of the following statements, if any, is *not* characteristic of human lungs?
   A. Both right and left lungs are composed of three lobes.
   B. Bronchi subdivide to form bronchioles.
   C. Capillary supply is abundant to facilitate gas exchange.
   D. All of the above statements are characteristic of human lungs.

6. Which body function is made possible by the existence of fibrous bands stretched across the larynx?
   A. Swallowing
   B. Breathing
   C. Diffusion
   D. Speech

7. The trachea is almost noncollapsible because of the presence of which of the following?
   A. Rings of cartilage
   B. Thyroid cartilage
   C. Epiglottis
   D. Vocal cords

8. Which of the following is true of the exchange of respiratory gases between lungs and blood?
   A. It takes place by diffusion.
   B. It is called *external respiration*.
   C. Both A and B are true.
   D. None of the above is true.

9. When the diaphragm contracts, which phase of ventilation is taking place?
   A. External respiration
   B. Expiration
   C. Internal respiration
   D. Inspiration

10. Which of the following is *not* characteristic of the nasal cavities?
    A. They contain many blood vessels that warm incoming air.
    B. They contain the adenoids.
    C. They are lined with mucous membranes.
    D. They are separated by a partition called the *nasal septum*.

Matching

Match each term in column A with its corresponding term in column B. (Only one answer is correct for each.)

Column A

_____ 11. Vocal cords
_____ 12. Pulmonary ventilation
_____ 13. Pleura
_____ 14. Pneumothorax
_____ 15. Emphysema
_____ 16. Throat
_____ 17. Ethmoidal
_____ 18. Windpipe
_____ 19. Alveoli
_____ 20. Surfactant

Column B

A. Serous membrane
B. Pharynx
C. Paranasal sinus
D. LVRS
E. Larynx
F. Diffusion
G. Collapsed lung
H. Trachea
I. Breathing
J. IRDS

SAGITTAL VIEW OF FACE AND NECK

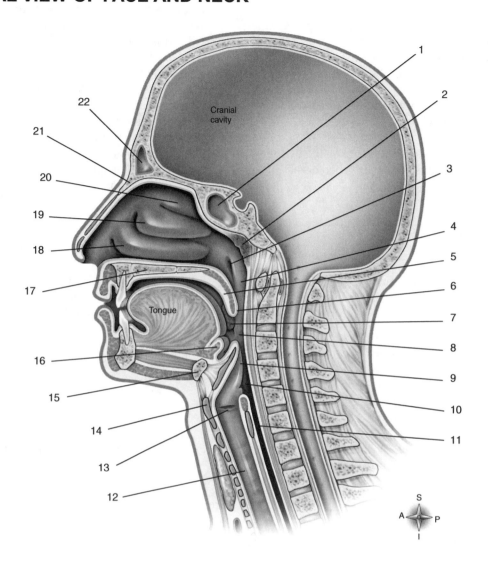

1. _____

2. _____

3. _____

4. _____

5. _____

6. _____

7. _____

8. _____

9. _____

10. _____

11. _____

12. _____

13. _____

14. _____

15. _____

16. _____

17. _____

18. _____

19. _____

20. _____

21. _____

22. _____

RESPIRATORY ORGANS

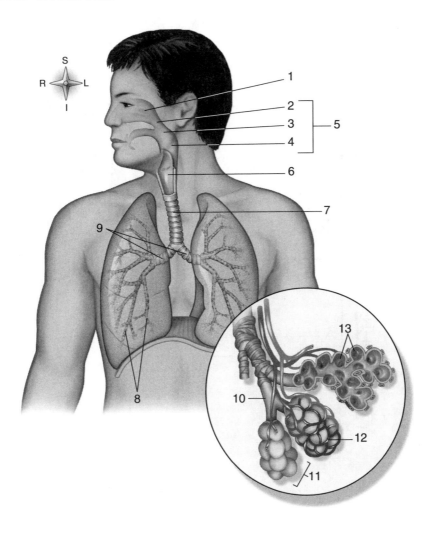

1. _____

2. _____

3. _____

4. _____

5. _____

6. _____

7. _____

8. _____

9. _____

10. _____

11. _____

12. _____

13. _____

PULMONARY VENTILATION VOLUMES

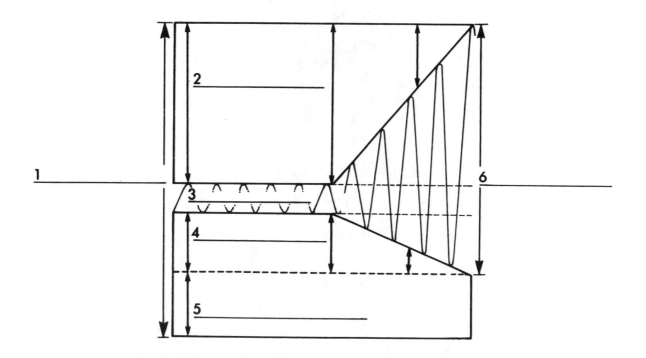

1. _____   4. _____

2. _____   5. _____

3. _____   6. _____

CHAPTER 17

The Digestive System

T hink of the last meal you ate. Imagine the different shapes, sizes, tastes, and textures that you so recently enjoyed. Think of those items circulating in your bloodstream in those same original shapes, sizes, and textures. Impossible? Of course! Because of this impossibility, you can begin to understand and marvel at the close relationship of the digestive system to the circulatory system. It is the digestive system that changes our food, both mechanically and chemically, into a form that is usable in the blood and the body.

This change in food begins the moment you take the very first bite. Digestion starts in the mouth, where food is chewed and mixed with saliva. It then moves down the pharynx and esophagus by peristalsis and enters the stomach. In the stomach it is churned and mixed with gastric juices to become chyme. The chyme goes from the stomach into the duodenum where it is further broken down chemically by intestinal fluids, bile, and pancreatic juice. Those secretions prepare the food for absorption all along the course of the small intestine. Products that are not absorbed pass on through the entire length of the small intestine (duodenum, jejunum, ileum). From there they enter into the cecum of the large intestine, continue on to the ascending colon, transverse colon, descending colon, and sigmoid colon, and finally into the rectum, and out the anus.

Products that are used in the cells undergo absorption. Absorption allows newly processed nutrients to pass through the walls of the digestive tract and into the bloodstream to be distributed to the cells.

Your review of this system will help you understand the mechanical and chemical processes necessary to convert food into energy sources and compounds necessary for survival.

TOPICS FOR REVIEW

Before progressing to Chapter 18, you should review the structure and function of all the organs of digestion. You should have an understanding of the process of digestion, both chemical and mechanical, and of the processes of absorption and metabolism.

THE DIGESTIVE SYSTEM
ORGANS OF THE DIGESTIVE SYSTEM

Fill in the blanks.

1. The organs of the digestive system form an irregular-shaped tube called the *alimentary canal* or
    _____ _____.

2. The churning of food in the stomach is an example of the _____ break-
    down of food.

3. _____ breakdown occurs when digestive enzymes act on food as it
    passes through the digestive tract.

4. Waste material resulting from the digestive process is known as _____.

5. Foods undergo three kinds of processing in the body: _____,
    _____, and _____.

*Identify which are main organs and which are accessory organs of the digestive system. Write the corre-
sponding letter in the answer blank.*

A. Main organ   B. Accessory organ

_____ 6.   Mouth

_____ 7.   Parotids

_____ 8.   Liver

_____ 9.   Stomach

_____ 10.   Cecum

_____ 11.   Esophagus

_____ 12.   Rectum

_____ 13.   Pharynx

_____ 14.   Appendix

_____ 15.   Teeth

_____ 16.   Gallbladder

_____ 17.   Pancreas

▶ *If you had difficulty with this section, review pages 487-488.*

MOUTH

TEETH

SALIVARY GLANDS

Circle the correct answer.

18. Which one of the following is *not* a part of the roof of the mouth?
    A. Uvula
    B. Palatine bones
    C. Maxillary bones
    D. Soft palate
    E. All of the above are part of the roof of the mouth.

19. The largest of the papillae on the surface of the tongue are the:
    A. Filiform
    B. Fungiform
    C. Vallate
    D. Taste buds

20. The first baby tooth, on average, appears at:
    A. 2 months
    B. 1 year
    C. 3 months
    D. 1 month
    E. 6 months

21. The portion of the tooth that is covered with enamel is the:
    A. Pulp cavity
    B. Neck
    C. Root
    D. Crown
    E. None of the above is correct.

22. The wall of the pulp cavity is surrounded by:
    A. Enamel
    B. Dentin
    C. Cementum
    D. Connective tissue
    E. Blood and lymphatic vessels

23. Which of the following teeth is missing from the deciduous arch?
    A. Central incisor
    B. Canine
    C. Second premolar
    D. First molar
    E. Second molar

24. The permanent central incisor erupts between the ages of _____.
    A. 9 and 13
    B. 5 and 6
    C. 7 and 10
    D. 7 and 8
    E. None of the above

25. The third molar appears between the ages of _____.
    A. 10 and 14
    B. 5 and 8
    C. 11 and 16
    D. 17 and 24
    E. None of the above

26. A general term for infection of the gums is:
    A. Dental caries
    B. Leukoplakia
    C. Vincent angina
    D. Gingivitis

27. The ducts of the _____ glands open into the floor of the mouth.
    A. Sublingual
    B. Submandibular
    C. Parotid
    D. Carotid

28. The volume of saliva secreted per day is about:
    A. One-half pint
    B. One pint
    C. One liter
    D. One gallon

29. Mumps are an infection of the:
    A. Parotid gland
    B. Sublingual gland
    C. Submandibular gland
    D. Tonsils

30. Incisors are used during mastication to:
    A. Cut
    B. Piece
    C. Tear
    D. Grind

31. Another name for the third molar is:
    A. Central incisor
    B. Wisdom tooth
    C. Canine
    D. Lateral incisor

32. After food has been chewed, it is formed into a small rounded mass called a:
    A. Moat
    B. Chyme
    C. Bolus
    D. Protease

 If you had difficulty with this section, review pages 488-495.

WALL OF DIGESTIVE TRACT

Fill in the blanks.

33. The serosa of the digestive tube is composed of the _____ _____ in the abdominal cavity.

34. The digestive tract extends from the _____ to the _____ .

35. The inside or hollow space within the alimentary canal is called the _____ .

36. The inside layer of the digestive tract is the _____ .

37. The connective tissue layer that lies beneath the lining of the digestive tract is the _____ .

38. The muscularis contracts and moves food through the gastrointestinal tract by a process known as _____ .

39. The outermost covering of the digestive tube is the _____ .

40. The loops of the digestive tract are anchored to the posterior wall of the abdominal cavity by the _____ .

PHARYNX

ESOPHAGUS

STOMACH

Fill in the blanks.

The (41) _____ is a tubelike structure that functions as part of both the respiratory and digestive systems. It connects the mouth with the (42) _____ . The esophagus serves as a passageway for movement of food from the pharynx to the (43) _____ . Food enters the stomach by passing through the muscular (44) _____ _____ at the end of the esophagus. Contraction of the stomach mixes the food thoroughly with the gastric juices and breaks it down into a semisolid mixture called (45) _____ . The three divisions of the stomach are the (46) _____ , (47) _____ , and (48) _____ . Food is held in the stomach by the (49) _____ _____ muscle long enough for partial digestion to occur. After food has been in the stomach for approximately 3 hours, the chyme will enter the (50) _____ _____ .

Match each term with its corresponding definition.

_____ 51. Stomach folds

_____ 52. Upper right border of stomach

_____ 53. Heartburn

_____ 54. 10-inch passageway

_____ 55. Shown to be an effective treatment of Crohn disease

_____ 56. Semisolid mixture of stomach contents

_____ 57. Muscle contractions of the digestive system

_____ 58. Craterlike wound in digestive system caused by tissue destruction

_____ 59. Stomach pushes through the gap in the diaphragm

_____ 60. Lower left border of stomach

A. Esophagus

B. Chyme

C. Peristalsis

D. Rugae

E. Ulcer

F. Greater curvature

G. Acid indigestion

H. Triple therapy

I. Hiatal hernia

J. Lesser curvature

▶ *If you had difficulty with this section, review pages 495-501.*

SMALL INTESTINE
LIVER AND GALLBLADDER
PANCREAS

Circle the correct answer.

61. Which one is *not* part of the small intestine?
    A. Jejunum
    B. Ileum
    C. Cecum
    D. Duodenum

62. Which one of the following structures does *not* increase the surface area of the intestine for absorption?
    A. Plicae
    B. Rugae
    C. Villi
    D. Brush border

63. The union of the cystic duct and hepatic duct form the:
    A. Common bile duct
    B. Major duodenal papilla
    C. Minor duodenal papilla
    D. Pancreatic duct

64. Obstruction of the _____ will lead to jaundice.
    A. Hepatic duct
    B. Pancreatic duct
    C. Cystic duct
    D. None of the above

65. Bile is responsible for the:
    A. Final digestion of fats
    B. Emulsification of fats
    C. Chemical breakdown of fats
    D. Chemical breakdown of cholesterol

66. The middle third of the duodenum contains the:
    A. Islets
    B. Fundus
    C. Body
    D. Rugae
    E. Major duodenal papilla

67. Cholelithiasis is the term used to describe:
    A. Biliary colic
    B. Jaundice
    C. Portal hypertension
    D. Gall stones

68. The liver is an:
    A. Enzyme
    B. Endocrine organ
    C. Endocrine gland
    D. Exocrine gland

69. Fats in chyme stimulate the secretion of the hormone:
    A. Lipase
    B. Cholecystokinin
    C. Protease
    D. Amylase

70. The largest gland in the body is the:
    A. Pituitary
    B. Thyroid
    C. Liver
    D. Thymus

▶ *If you had difficulty with this section, review pages 501-508.*

LARGE INTESTINE

APPENDIX

PERITONEUM

If the statement is true, write "T" in the answer blank. If the statement is false, correct the statement by circling the incorrect term and writing the correct term in the answer blank.

_____ 71. Bacteria in the large intestine are responsible for the synthesis of vitamin E needed for normal blood clotting.

_____ 72. Villi in the large intestine absorb salts and water.

_____ 73. If waste products pass rapidly through the large intestine, constipation results.

_____ 74. The ileocecal valve opens into the sigmoid colon.

_____ 75. The splenic flexure is the bend between the ascending colon and the transverse colon.

_____ 76. The splenic colon is the S-shaped segment that terminates in the rectum.

_____ 77. The appendix serves no important digestive function in humans.

_____ 78. Appendicitis is more common in children and young adults because the lumen of the appendix is larger during that period making it easier for food and fecal material to become trapped.

_____ 79. The visceral layer of the peritoneum lines the abdominal cavity.

_____ 80. The greater omentum is shaped like a fan and serves to anchor the small intestine to the posterior abdominal wall.

_____ 81. Diarrhea is an inflammation of abnormal saclike outpouchings of the intestinal wall.

_____ 82. Crohn disease is a type of autoimmune colitis.

_____ 83. A colostomy is a surgical procedure in which an artificial anus is created on the abdominal wall.

_____ 84. Peritonitis is the abnormal accumulation of fluid in the peritoneal space.

▶ *If you had difficulty with this section, review pages 508-513.*

DIGESTION

ABSORPTION

Circle the correct answer.

85. Which one of the following substances does *not* contain any enzymes?
    A. Saliva
    B. Bile
    C. Gastric juice
    D. Pancreatic juice
    E. Intestinal juice

86. Which one of the following is a simple sugar?
    A. Maltose
    B. Sucrose
    C. Lactose
    D. Glucose
    E. Starch

87. Cane sugar is the same as:
    A. Maltose
    B. Lactose
    C. Sucrose
    D. Glucose
    E. None of the above

88. Most of the digestion of carbohydrates takes place in the:
    A. Mouth
    B. Stomach
    C. Small intestine
    D. Large intestine

89. Fats are broken down into:
    A. Amino acids
    B. Simple sugars
    C. Fatty acids
    D. Disaccharides

▷ *If you had difficulty with this section, review pages 513-516.*

CHEMICAL DIGESTION

90. Fill in the blank areas on the chart below.

DIGESTIVE JUICES AND ENZYMES	SUBSTANCE DIGESTED (OR HYDROLYZED)	RESULTING PRODUCT
Saliva		
1. Amylase	1.	1. Maltose
Gastric Juice		
2. Protease (pepsin) plus hydrochloric acid	2. Proteins	2.
Pancreatic Juice		
3. Protease (trypsin)	3. Proteins (intact or partially digested)	3.
4. Lipase	4.	4. Fatty acids, monoglycerides, and glycerol
5. Amylase	5.	5. Maltose
Intestinal Juice		
6. Peptidases	6.	6. Amino acids
7.	7. Sucrose	7. Glucose and fructose
8. Lactase	8.	8. Glucose and galactose (simple sugars)
9. Maltase	9. Maltose	9.

▶ *If you had difficulty with this section, review page 515.*

UNSCRAMBLE THE WORDS

91. **S L B O U**

☐ ◯ ◯ ☐ ☐

92. **E Y C H M**

◯ ☐ ☐ ☐ ◯

93. **L L A A P P I**

☐ ◯ ☐ ☐ ☐ ◯

94. **P M E R T E U I O N**

◯ ☐ ◯ ☐ ☐ ◯ ☐ ☐ ☐

Take the circled letters, unscramble them, and fill in the solution.

What the groom gave his bride after the wedding.

95. ☐☐☐☐☐   ☐☐☐☐☐☐

APPLYING WHAT YOU KNOW

96. Mr. Amoto was a successful businessman, but he worked too hard and was always under great stress. He took high doses of aspirin, almost daily, to relieve his stress headaches. His doctor cautioned him that if he did not alter his style of living, he would be subject to hyperacidity. What could be a result of hyperacidity?

97. Baby Nicholas has been regurgitating his bottle feeding at every meal. The milk is curdled, but does not appear to be digested. He has become dehydrated, and so his mother, Bobbi, is taking him to the pediatrician. What would you guess is a possible diagnosis based on what you have learned from your textbook reading?

98. Mr. Lynch has high cholesterol. In an effort to lower his cholesterol, he quickly lost 25 pounds by consuming an ultra low-fat diet. Since then he has noticed a yellowish cast to his skin and has periodic pain in the right upper quadrant of the abdominopelvic region. What is a possible diagnosis for Mr. Lynch? What is the name of the surgical procedure that may be performed on Mr. Lynch?

99.   Word Find

Find and circle 22 terms presented in this chapter. Words may be spelled top to bottom, bottom to top, right to left, left to right, or diagonally.

```
X M E T A B O L I S M X X W
R S D P E R I S T A L S I S
E V A M N O I T S E G I D R
E D E E U O Q T W Q O H N Q
Q Z H S R N I N T F E C E S
D H R E C C I T K C J A P E
Q W R N A T N V P Y R M P C
O C A T N R B A P R H O A I
U Y I E O W T A P A O T W D
B O D R L N P B F Q J S V N
N T S Y F I S L U M E E B U
W G J A L U V U N R N W O A
Q S N L X D U O D E N U M J
H C A V I T Y M U C O S A D
Y E A A P H V W S V C Q J C
```

Absorption	Emulsify	Mucosa
Appendix	Feces	Pancreas
Cavity	Fundus	Papillae
Crown	Heartburn	Peristalsis
Dentin	Jaundice	Stomach
Diarrhea	Mastication	Uvula
Digestion	Mesentery	
Duodenum	Metabolism	

DID YOU KNOW?

The liver performs over 500 functions and produces over 1000 enzymes to handle the chemical conversions necessary for survival.

About 20% of older adults have diabetes, and almost 40% have some impaired glucose tolerance.

The human stomach lining replaces itself every 3 days.

DIGESTIVE SYSTEM

Fill in the crossword puzzle.

ACROSS

5. Digested food moves from intestine to blood
8. Semisolid mixture
9. Inflammation of the appendix
11. Rounded mass of food
13. Stomach folds

DOWN

1. Yellowish skin discoloration
2. Process of chewing
3. Fluid stools
4. Movement of food through digestive tract
6. Vomitus
7. Waste product of digestion
10. Intestinal folds
12. Open wound in digestive area acted on by acid juices
14. Prevents food from entering nasal cavities

CHECK YOUR KNOWLEDGE

Multiple Choice

Circle the correct answer.

1. During the process of digestion, *stored* bile is poured into the duodenum by which of the following?
   A. Gallbladder
   B. Liver
   C. Pancreas
   D. Spleen

2. Which portion of the alimentary canal mixes food with gastric juice and breaks it down into a mixture called *chyme*?
   A. Gallbladder
   B. Small intestine
   C. Stomach
   D. Large intestine

3. What is the middle portion of the small intestine called?
   A. Jejunum
   B. Ileum
   C. Duodenum
   D. Cecum

4. The crown of the tooth is covered externally with which of the following?
   A. Cementum
   B. Enamel
   C. Dentin
   D. Pulp

5. What is the layer of tissue that forms the outermost covering of organs found in the digestive tract called?
   A. Mucosa
   B. Serosa
   C. Submucosa
   D. Muscularis

6. Duodenal ulcers appear in which of the following?
   A. Stomach
   B. Small intestine
   C. Large intestine
   D. Esophagus

7. What is an extension of the peritoneum that is shaped like a giant pleated fan?
   A. Omentum
   B. Mesentery
   C. Peritoneal cavity
   D. Ligament

8. Protein digestion begins in the:
   A. Esophagus
   B. Small intestine
   C. Stomach
   D. Large intestine

9. The enzyme pepsin is concerned primarily with the digestion of which of the following?
   A. Sugars
   B. Starches
   C. Proteins
   D. Fats

10. The enzyme amylase converts which of the following?
    A. Starches to sugars
    B. Sugars to starches
    C. Proteins to amino acids
    D. Fatty acids and glycerol to fats

Completion

Fill in the blanks using the terms listed below. Write the corresponding letter in each blank.

A. Ileum
B. Amylase
C. Muscularis
D. Metabolism
E. Cholecystokinin
F. Molars

G. Lower esophageal sphincter
H. Digestion
I. Incisors
J. Greater omentum
K. Absorption
L. Adventitia

M. Upper esophageal sphincter
N. Sigmoid colon
O. Canines
P. Amino acids
Q. Duodenum
R. Jejunum

S. Premolars
T. Mucosa
U. Submucosa
V. Cecum
W. Bile
X. Serosa

11. The S-shaped portion of the colon is called the _____.

12. The portion of the peritoneum that descends from the stomach and the transverse colon to form a lacy apron of fat over the intestines is called the _____.

13. The "building blocks" of protein molecules are _____.

14. The small intestine is made up of three sections called the _____, _____, and the _____.

15. Fats that enter into the digestive tract are emulsified when they are acted on by a substance called _____.

16. Foods undergo three kinds of processing in the body: _____, _____, and _____.

17. Fats in the chyme stimulate the secretion of _____, which stimulates contraction of the gallbladder to release bile.

18. The four tissue layers that make up the wall of the digestive tract are the _____, _____, _____, and _____.

19. Food enters the stomach by passing through a muscular structure at the end of the esophagus. This structure is called the _____.

20. The four major types of teeth found in the human mouth are _____, _____, _____, and _____.

LOCATION OF DIGESTIVE ORGANS

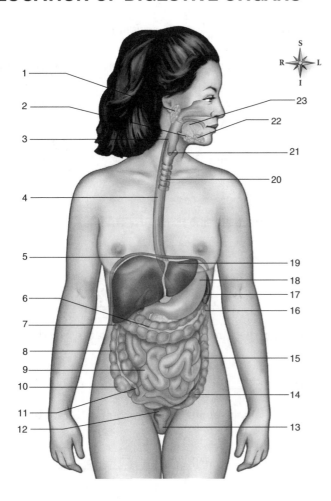

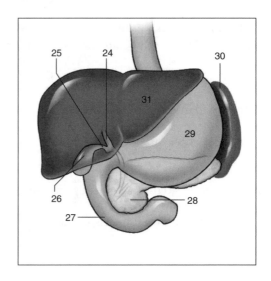

1. _____
2. _____
3. _____
4. _____
5. _____
6. _____
7. _____
8. _____
9. _____
10. _____
11. _____
12. _____
13. _____
14. _____
15. _____
16. _____

17. _____
18. _____
19. _____
20. _____
21. _____
22. _____
23. _____
24. _____
25. _____
26. _____
27. _____
28. _____
29. _____
30. _____
31. _____

TOOTH

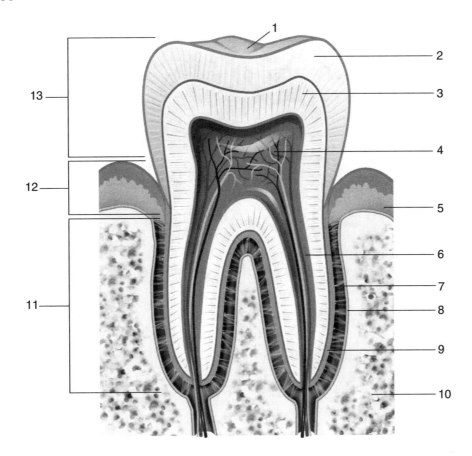

1. _____   8. _____

2. _____   9. _____

3. _____   10. _____

4. _____   11. _____

5. _____   12. _____

6. _____   13. _____

7. _____

THE SALIVARY GLANDS

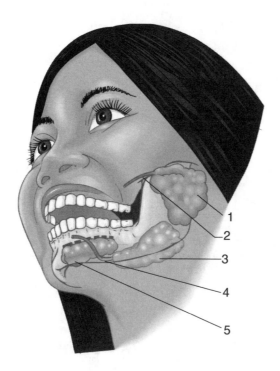

1. _____   4. _____

2. _____   5. _____

3. _____

STOMACH

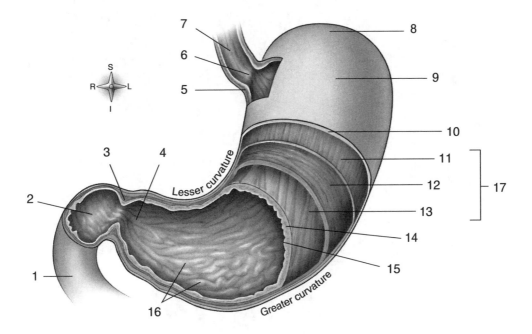

1. _____   10. _____

2. _____   11. _____

3. _____   12. _____

4. _____   13. _____

5. _____   14. _____

6. _____   15. _____

7. _____   16. _____

8. _____   17. _____

9. _____

GALLBLADDER AND BILE DUCTS

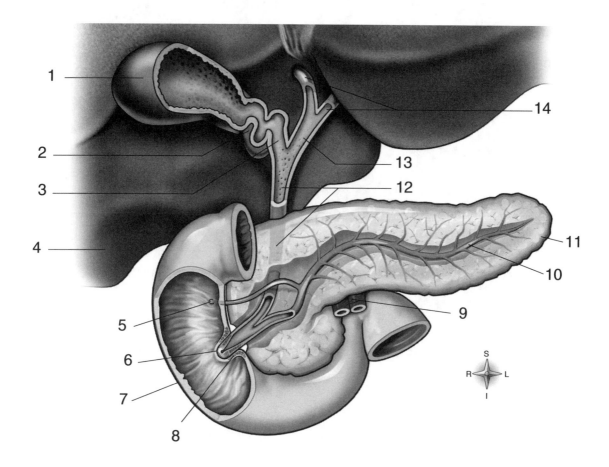

1. _____   8. _____

2. _____   9. _____

3. _____   10. _____

4. _____   11. _____

5. _____   12. _____

6. _____   13. _____

7. _____   14. _____

THE SMALL INTESTINE

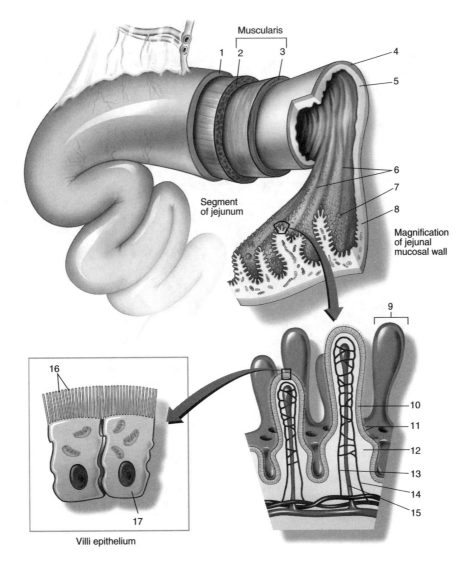

Muscularis

Segment of jejunum

Magnification of jejunal mucosal wall

Villi epithelium

1. _____

2. _____

3. _____

4. _____

5. _____

6. _____

7. _____

8. _____

9. _____

10. _____

11. _____

12. _____

13. _____

14. _____

15. _____

16. _____

17. _____

THE LARGE INTESTINE

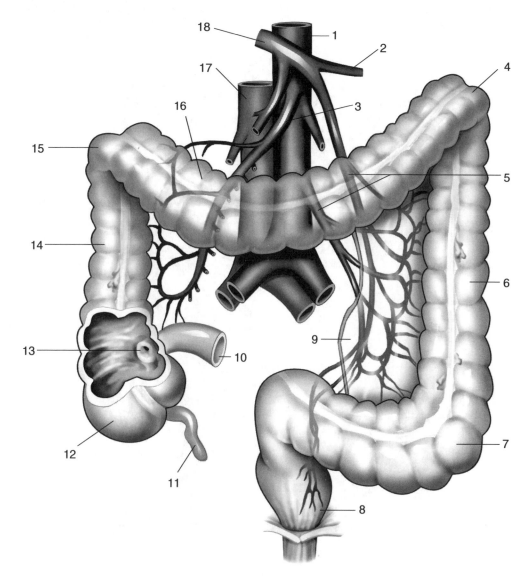

1. _____

2. _____

3. _____

4. _____

5. _____

6. _____

7. _____

8. _____

9. _____

10. _____

11. _____

12. _____

13. _____

14. _____

15. _____

16. _____

17. _____

18. _____

• CHAPTER 18

Nutrition and Metabolism

Most of us love to eat, but do the foods we enjoy provide us with the basic food types necessary for good nutrition? The body, a finely tuned machine, requires a balance of carbohydrates, fats, proteins, vitamins, and minerals to function properly. These nutrients must be digested, absorbed, and circulated to cells constantly to accommodate the numerous activities that occur throughout the body. The use the body makes of foods once these processes are completed is called *metabolism*.

The liver plays a major role in the metabolism of food. It helps maintain a normal blood glucose level, removes toxins from the blood, processes blood immediately after it leaves the gastrointestinal tract, and initiates the first steps of protein and fat metabolism.

This chapter also discusses basal metabolic rate (BMR). The BMR is the rate at which food is catabolized under basal conditions. This test and the protein-bound iodine (PBI) are indirect measures of thyroid gland functioning. The total metabolic rate (TMR) is the amount of energy, expressed in calories, used by the body each day.

Finally, maintaining a constant body temperature is a function of the hypothalamus and a challenge for the metabolic mechanisms of the body. Review of this chapter is necessary to provide you with an understanding of the "fuel" (nutrition) requirements necessary to maintain this complex homeostatic machine—the body.

TOPICS FOR REVIEW

Before progressing to Chapter 19, you should be able to define and contrast catabolism and anabolism. Your review should include the metabolic roles of carbohydrates, fats, proteins, vitamins, and minerals. Your study should conclude with an understanding of the basal metabolic rate, physiological mechanisms that regulate body temperature, and the common metabolic and eating disorders.

METABOLIC FUNCTIONS OF THE LIVER

Fill in the blanks.

The liver plays an important role in the mechanical digestion of lipids because it secretes
(1) _____. It also produces two of the plasma proteins that play an essential
role in blood clotting. These two proteins are (2) _____ and
(3) _____. Additionally, liver cells store several substances, notably vitamins A and D and (4) _____. Finally, the liver is assisted by a unique structural feature of the blood vessels that supply it. This arrangement, known as the
(5) _____ _____
_____ , allows toxins to be removed from the bloodstream before nutrients
are distributed throughout the body.

NUTRIENT METABOLISM

Match each term with its corresponding definition. (Answers may be used more than once.)

_____ 6. Used if cells have inadequate amounts of glucose to catabolize

_____ 7. Preferred energy food

_____ 8. Amino acids

_____ 9. Fat soluble

_____ 10. Required for nerve conduction

_____ 11. Glycolysis

_____ 12. Inorganic elements found naturally in the earth

_____ 13. Pyruvic acid

A. Carbohydrate

B. Fat

C. Protein

D. Vitamins

E. Minerals

Circle the term in each word group that does not belong.

14. Glycolysis	Citric acid cycle	ATP	Bile
15. Adipose	Amino acids	Triglycerides	Lipid
16. A	D	M	K
17. Iron	Proteins	Amino acids	Essential
18. Hydrocortisone	Insulin	Growth hormone	Epinephrine
19. Sodium	Calcium	Zinc	Folic acid
20. Thiamine	Niacin	Ascorbic acid	Riboflavin

▶ *If you had difficulty with this section, review pages 525-532.*

METABOLIC RATES

Circle the correct answer.

21. The rate at which food is catabolized under
    basal conditions is the:
    A. TMR
    B. PBI
    C. BMR
    D. ATP

22. The total amount of energy used by the body
    per day is the:
    A. TMR
    B. PBI
    C. BMR
    D. ATP

23. A/an _____ is the amount of energy needed to raise the temperature of 1 gram of water 1° Celsius.
    A. Calorie
    B. Kilocalorie
    C. ATP
    D. BMR

24. Which of the following is a factor when determining the BMR?
    A. Sex
    B. Age
    C. Size
    D. All of the above

25. Which of the following is a factor when determining the TMR?
    A. Exercise
    B. Food intake
    C. Environmental temperature
    D. All of the above

▶ *If you had difficulty with this section, review page 532.*

METABOLIC AND EATING DISORDERS

Match each description with its related term. Write the corresponding letter in the answer blank.

_____ 26. Insulin deficiency is a symptom of this disorder

_____ 27. Behavioral disorder characterized by chronic refusal to eat

_____ 28. An advanced form of PCM

_____ 29. Results from a deficiency of calories in general and protein in particular

_____ 30. Hypothyroidism will affect this measurement

_____ 31. Abdominal bloating

_____ 32. Symptom of chronic overeating behavior

_____ 33. Behavioral disorder characterized by insatiable craving for food alternating with periods of self-deprivation

A. BMR

B. Diabetes mellitus

C. Anorexia nervosa

D. Bulimia

E. Obesity

F. PCM

G. Marasmus

H. Ascites

▶ *If you had difficulty with this section, review pages 532-534.*

BODY TEMPERATURES

Circle the correct answer.

34. Over _____ of the energy released from food molecules during catabolism is converted to heat rather than being transferred to ATP.
    A. 20%
    B. 40%
    C. 60%
    D. 80%

35. Maintaining thermoregulation is a function of the:
    A. Thalamus
    B. Hypothalamus
    C. Thyroid
    D. Parathyroids

36. Transfer of heat energy to the skin, then the external environment is known as:
    A. Radiation
    B. Conduction
    C. Convection
    D. Evaporation

37. A flow of heat waves away from the blood is known as:
    A. Radiation
    B. Conduction
    C. Convection
    D. Evaporation

38. A transfer of heat energy to air that is continually flowing away from the skin is known as:
   A. Radiation
   B. Conduction
   C. Convection
   D. Evaporation

39. Heat that is absorbed by the process of water vaporization is called:
   A. Radiation
   B. Conduction
   C. Convection
   D. Evaporation

▶ *If you had difficulty with this section, review pages 534-535.*

ABNORMAL BODY TEMPERATURE

If the statement is true, write "T" in the answer blank. If the statement is false, correct the statement by circling the incorrect term and writing the correct term in the answer blank.

_____ 40. Pyrogens cause the thermostatic control centers of the hypothalamus to produce a fever.

_____ 41. Malignant hyperthermia is the inability to maintain a normal body temperature in extremely cold environments.

_____ 42. Frostbite is local damage to tissues caused by extremely low temperatures.

_____ 43. Heat exhaustion is characterized by body temperatures of 41° Celsius or higher.

_____ 44. Dantrium is used to prevent or relieve the effects of frostbite.

▶ *If you had difficulty with this section, review pages 535-537.*

UNSCRAMBLE THE WORDS

45. **L R I E V**

   ☐☐◯◯◯☐

46. **T A O B A L I C M S**

   ☐◯◯☐◯☐☐☐☐

47. **O M N I A**

   ◯☐☐◯◯

48. **Y P U R C V I**

   ◯☐☐☐◯☐☐

Take the circled letters, unscramble them, and fill in the solution.

How the magician paid his bills.

49. ☐☐☐☐☐☐☐☐☐☐☐☐

APPLYING WHAT YOU KNOW

50. Dr. Carey was concerned about Deborah. Her daily food intake provided fewer calories than her TMR. If this trend continues, what will be the result? If it continues over a long time, what eating disorder might Deborah develop?

51. Kathryn had been experiencing fatigue, and a blood test revealed that she was slightly anemic. What mineral will her doctor most likely prescribe? What dietary sources might you suggest that she emphasize in her daily intake?

52. Joe was training daily for an upcoming marathon. Three days before the 25-mile event, he suddenly quit his daily routine of jogging and switched to a diet high in carbohydrates. Why did Joe suddenly switch his routine of training?

53.   Word Find

Find and circle 18 terms presented in this chapter. Words may be spelled top to bottom, bottom to top, right to left, left to right, or diagonally.

```
C  C  C  B  W  E  F  F  L  J  V  G  G  S
A  T  N  L  W  E  U  O  Z  I  E  L  I  B
R  K  K  P  Z  F  R  I  T  P  O  Y  K  L
B  Q  M  I  N  E  R  A  L  S  J  C  C  P
O  S  S  N  C  X  M  I  D  B  D  O  W  P
H  S  I  Y  O  I  T  X  H  I  N  L  S  N
Y  E  L  N  N  I  K  W  W  D  S  Y  N  S
D  G  O  S  O  W  T  I  U  E  H  S  C  N
R  M  B  Y  T  I  W  C  Z  N  N  I  A  A
A  R  A  Q  W  A  T  B  E  I  G  S  J  M
T  E  T  F  N  I  F  A  E  V  E  W  T  Y
E  V  A  P  O  R  A  T  I  O  N  D  T  E
S  I  C  N  E  S  O  P  I  D  A  O  F  E
H  L  Y  K  I  R  E  B  V  P  A  H  C  J
I  W  E  E  P  A  D  F  T  E  A  R  G  G
```

ATP	Conduction	Liver
Adipose	Convection	Minerals
BMR	Evaporation	Proteins
Bile	Fats	Radiation
Carbohydrates	Glycerol	TMR
Catabolism	Glycolysis	Vitamins

DID YOU KNOW?

The amount of energy required for a person to raise a 200-pound man 15 feet in the air is about the amount of energy in one large calorie.

NUTRITION/METABOLISM

Fill in the crossword puzzle.

ACROSS

1. Breaks food molecules down releasing stored energy
4. Amount of energy needed to raise the temperature of one gram of water 1° Celsius
7. Rate of metabolism when a person is lying down, but awake (abbreviation)
8. A series of reactions that join glucose molecules together to form glycogen
10. Builds food molecules into complex substances

DOWN

2. Occurs when food molecules enter cells and undergo many chemical changes there
3. Organic molecule needed in small quantities for normal metabolism throughout the body
5. Oxygen-using
6. A unit of measure for heat, also known as a large calorie
9. Takes place in the cytoplasm of a cell and changes glucose to pyruvic acid

CHECK YOUR KNOWLEDGE

Multiple Choice

Circle the correct answer.

1. The citric acid cycle changes acetyl CoA to:
    A. Oxygen
    B. Carbon dioxide
    C. Pyruvic acid
    D. Glucose

2. The anabolism of glucose produces which of the following?
    A. Glycogen
    B. Amino acid
    C. Rennin
    D. Starch

3. Which of the following is a major hormone in the body that aids carbohydrate metabolism?
    A. Oxytocin
    B. Epinephrine
    C. Insulin
    D. Growth hormone

4. The total metabolic rate is which of the following?
    A. The amount of fats a person consumes in a 24-hour period
    B. The same as the BMR
    C. The amount of energy expressed in calories used by the body per day
    D. Cannot be calculated

5. When your consumption of calories equals your TMR, your weight will do which of the following?
    A. Increase
    B. Remain the same
    C. Fluctuate
    D. Decrease

6. Which of the following is a normal glucose level?
    A. 40 to 80 mg/100 mL blood
    B. 80 to 120 mg/100 mL blood
    C. 100 to 140 mg/100 mL blood
    D. 180 to 220 mg/100 mL blood

7. When glucose is *not* available, the body will next catabolize which of the following energy sources?
    A. Fats
    B. Proteins
    C. Minerals
    D. Vitamins

8. Maintaining the homeostasis of the body temperature is the responsibility of which of the following?
    A. Hypothalamus
    B. Environmental condition in which we live
    C. Circulatory system
    D. None of the above

9. The liver plays an important role in the mechanical digestion of lipids because it secretes:
    A. Glucose molecules
    B. Bile
    C. Glycogen
    D. Citric acid

10. What is the primary molecule the body usually breaks down as an energy source?
    A. Amino acid
    B. Pepsin
    C. Maltose
    D. Glucose

Completion

Complete the following statements using the terms listed below. (Some words may be used more than once.) Write the corresponding letter in the answer blank.

A. Vitamins
B. Insulin
C. Carbohydrates
D. Fats
E. Glycolysis
F. Metabolism

G. ATP
H. Sodium
I. Proteins
J. Citric acid cycle
K. Calcium
L. Glycogen loading

11. Proper nutrition requires the balance of the three basic food types: _____, _____, and _____.

12. The process that changes glucose to pyruvic acid is called _____.

13. Once glucose has been changed to pyruvic acid, another process in which pyruvic acid is changed to carbon dioxide takes place. This reaction is known as the _____.

14. A direct source of energy for doing cellular work is _____.

15. The only hormone that lowers blood glucose level is _____.

16. When cells have an inadequate amount of glucose to catabolize they will catabolize _____.

17. Some athletes consume large amounts of carbohydrates 2 to 3 days before an athletic event to store glycogen in skeletal muscles. This practice is called _____.

18. Organic molecules needed in small amounts for normal metabolism are _____.

19. Two minerals necessary for nerve conduction and contraction of muscle fibers are _____ and _____.

20. The "use of foods" is known as _____.

NEPHRON

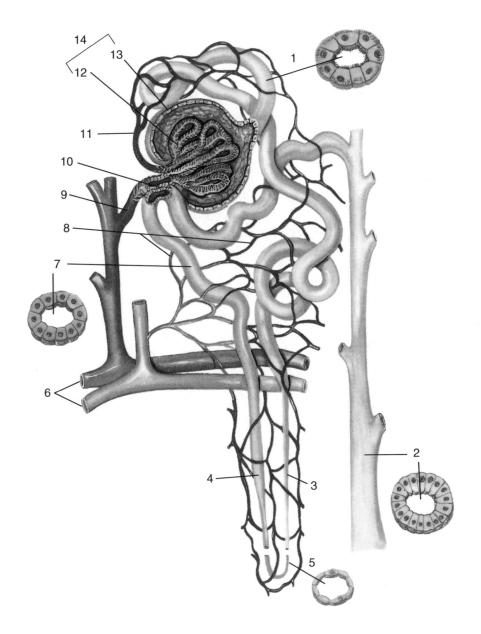

1. _____

2. _____

3. _____

4. _____

5. _____

6. _____

7. _____

8. _____

9. _____

10. _____

11. _____

12. _____

13. _____

14. _____

CHAPTER 20

Fluid and Electrolyte Balance

Referring to the first chapter in your text, you will recall that survival depends on the body's ability to maintain or restore homeostasis. Specifically, *homeostasis* means that the body fluids remain constant within very narrow limits. These fluids are classified as either intracellular fluid (ICF) or extracellular fluid (ECF). As their names imply, intracellular fluid lies within the cells and extracellular fluid is located outside the cells. A balance between these two fluids is maintained by certain body mechanisms. They are (1) the adjustment of fluid output to fluid intake under normal circumstances; (2) the concentration of electrolytes in the extracellular fluid; (3) the capillary blood pressure; and finally, (4) the concentration of proteins in the blood.

Comprehension of how these mechanisms maintain and restore fluid balance is necessary for an understanding of the complexities of homeostasis and its relationship to the survival of the individual.

TOPICS FOR REVIEW

Before progressing to Chapter 21, you should review the types of body fluids and their subdivisions. Your study should include the mechanisms that maintain fluid balance and the nature and importance of electrolytes in body fluids. You should be able to give examples of common fluid imbalances, and have an understanding of the role of fluid and electrolyte balance in the maintenance of homeostasis.

BODY FLUIDS

Circle the correct answer.

1. The largest volume of water in the body by far lies (*inside* or *outside*) cells.

2. Interstitial fluid is (*intracellular* or *extracellular*).

3. Plasma is (*intracellular* or *extracellular*).

4. Obese people have a (*lower* or *higher*) water content per pound of body weight than thin people.

5. Infants have (*more* or *less*) water in comparison to body weight than adults of either sex.

6. There is a rapid (*increase* or *decline*) in the proportion of body water to body weight during the first 10 years of life.

7. The female body contains slightly (*more* or *less*) water per pound of weight.

8. In general, as age increases, the amount of water per pound of body weight (*increases* or *decreases*).

9. Excluding adipose tissue, approximately (55% or 85%) of body weight is water.

10. The term (*fluid balance* or *fluid compartments*) means the volumes of ICF, IF, plasma, and the total volume of water in the body all remain relatively constant.

 If you had difficulty with this section, review pages 569-571.

MECHANISMS THAT MAINTAIN FLUID BALANCE

Circle the correct answer.

11. Which one of the following is *not* a positively charged ion?
    A. Chloride
    B. Calcium
    C. Sodium
    D. Potassium

12. Which one of the following is *not* a negatively charged ion?
    A. Chloride
    B. Bicarbonate
    C. Phosphate
    D. Sodium

13. The most abundant electrolyte in blood plasma is:
    A. NaCl
    B. KMg
    C. HCO_3
    D. HPO_4
    E. $CaPO_4$

14. What source contributes the least amount of water in the body?
    A. Water in foods that are eaten
    B. Ingested liquids
    C. Water formed from catabolism
    D. None of the above

15. The greatest amount of water lost from the body comes from the:
    A. Lungs
    B. Skin by diffusion
    C. Skin by sweat
    D. Feces
    E. Kidneys

16. Which one of the following is *not* a major factor that influences extracellular and intracellular fluid volumes?
    A. Concentration of electrolytes in the extracellular fluid
    B. Capillary blood pressure
    C. Concentration of proteins in blood
    D. All of the above are important factors

17. The fluid output source that changes the most is:
    A. Water loss in the feces
    B. Water loss from the skin
    C. Water loss via the lungs
    D. Water loss in the urine
    E. None of the above

18. The chief regulators of sodium within the body are the:
    A. Lungs
    B. Sweat glands
    C. Kidneys
    D. Large intestine
    E. None of the above

19. Which of the following is *not* correct?
    A. Fluid output must equal fluid intake.
    B. ADH controls salt reabsorption in the kidney.
    C. Water follows sodium.
    D. Renal tubule regulation of salt and water is the most important factor in determining urine volume.
    E. All of the above are correct.

20. Diuretics work on all but which one of the following?
    A. Proximal tubule
    B. Henle loop
    C. Distal tubule
    D. Collecting ducts
    E. Diuretics work on all of the above

21. Of all the sodium-containing secretions, the one with the largest volume is:
    A. Saliva
    B. Gastric secretions
    C. Bile
    D. Pancreatic juice
    E. Intestinal secretions

22. The higher the capillary blood pressure, the
_____ the amount of interstitial fluid.
A. Smaller
B. Larger
C. There is no relationship between capillary
blood pressure and volume of interstitial
fluid.

23. An increase in capillary blood pressure will
lead to _____ in blood volume.
A. An increase
B. A decrease
C. No change
D. None of the above

24. Which one of the fluid compartments varies the
most in volume?
A. Intracellular
B. Interstitial
C. Extracellular
D. Plasma

If the statement is true, write "T" in the answer blank. If the statement is false, correct the statement by circling the incorrect term and writing the correct term in the answer blank.

_____ 25. The three sources of fluid intake are the liquids we drink, the foods we eat, and water formed by the anabolism of foods.

_____ 26. The body maintains fluid balance mainly by changing the volume of urine excreted to match changes in the volume of fluid intake.

_____ 27. Some output of fluid will occur as long as life continues.

_____ 28. Glucose is an example of an electrolyte.

_____ 29. Where sodium goes, water soon follows.

_____ 30. Excess aldosterone leads to hypovolemia.

_____ 31. Diuretics have their effect on glomerular function.

_____ 32. Typical daily intake and output totals should be approximately 1200 mL.

_____ 33. Bile is a sodium-containing internal secretion.

_____ 34. The average daily diet contains about 500 mEq of sodium.

▶ *If you had difficulty with this section, review pages 571-578.*

FLUID IMBALANCES

Fill in the blanks.

(35) _____ is the fluid imbalance seen most often. In this condition, interstitial fluid volume (36) _____ first, but eventually, if treatment has not been given, intracellular fluid and plasma volumes (37) _____.

(38) _____ can also occur, but is much less common. Giving

(39) _____ _____ too rapidly or in too large amounts can put too heavy a burden on the (40) _____.

(41) _____ describes a blood sodium level above 145 mEq/L.

(42) _____ is a clinical term used to describe blood potassium levels above 5.1 mEq/L.

▶ *If you had difficulty with this section, review pages 577-580.*

UNSCRAMBLE THE WORDS

43. **M D E E A**

⬜⬜⬜⬜⬜

44. **D F I L U**

⬜⬜⬜⬜⬜

45. **N I O**

⬜⬜⬜

46. **S O U I T N V A R E N**

⬜⬜⬜⬜⬜⬜⬜⬜⬜⬜

Take the circled letters, unscramble them, and fill in the solution.

What Gary's dad disliked most about his music.

47. ⬜⬜⬜⬜⬜⬜

APPLYING WHAT YOU KNOW

48. Mrs. Titus was asked to keep an accurate record of her fluid intake and output. She was concerned because the two did not balance. What is a possible explanation for this?

49. Nurse Briker was caring for a patient who was receiving diuretics. What special nursing implications should be followed for patients being given this therapy?

50. Jack Sprat was 6'5" and weighed 185 lbs. His wife was 5'6" and weighed 185 lbs. Whose body contained more water?

51. Word Find

Find and circle 12 terms presented in this chapter. Words may be spelled top to bottom, bottom to top, right to left, left to right, or diagonally.

```
S T V H O M E O S T A S I S H
I E D E M A S Q A L P U E G L
M M L U F L U I D O Y O I S L
W S B E A E C O L D P N I E R
L I T A C V S H Q O C E H B C
L L X J L T E A W Y B V Q Q O
I O O P E A R U C T C A A R I
N B H R X S N O I I P R T C N
S A O X M G J C L N J T B A H
I N X X D V U D E Y K N Y O C
E A A J Q D I U R E T I C S X
I F C J A M P V E N B E Y F W
V F K T Q X R M D D S I V O T
E T T Z N T R P X I M L J F I
S W Y A P V Q N S K T K W B P
```

Aldosterone Edema Imbalance
Anabolism Electrolyte Intravenous
Catabolism Fluid Ions
Diuretics Homeostasis Kidney

DID YOU KNOW?

The best fluid replacement drink is 1/4 tsp. of table salt added to 1 quart of water.

If all of the water were drained from the body of an average 160-pound man, the body would weigh 64 pounds.

FLUID/ELECTROLYTES

Fill in the crossword puzzle.

ACROSS

3. Result of rapidly given intravenous fluids
4. Result of large loss of body fluids
5. Compound that dissociates in solution into ions
7. To break up
9. A subdivision of extracellular fluid (abbreviation)

DOWN

1. Organic substance that doesn't dissociate in solution
2. Dissociated particles of an electrolyte that carry an electrical charge
5. Fluid outside cells (abbreviation)
6. "Causing urine"
8. Fluid inside cells (abbreviation)

CHECK YOUR KNOWLEDGE

Multiple Choice

Circle the correct answer.

1. Which of the following statements, if any, is *false*?
   A. The more fat present in the body, the more total water content per unit of weight.
   B. The body weight of infants is composed of a higher percentage of water in comparison with the body weight of adults.
   C. As age increases, the amount of water per pound of body weight decreases.
   D. All of the above statements are true.

2. Avenues of fluid output include which of the following?
   A. Skin
   B. Lungs
   C. Kidneys
   D. All of the above

3. Excessive water loss and fluid imbalance can result from which of the following?
   A. Diarrhea
   B. Vomiting
   C. Severe burns
   D. All of the above

4. What factor is primarily responsible for moving water from interstitial fluid into blood?
   A. Aldosterone secretions
   B. Pressure in blood capillaries
   C. Protein concentration of blood plasma
   D. Antidiuretic hormone secretions

5. What is the chief regulator of sodium levels in body fluids?
   A. Kidney
   B. Intestine
   C. Blood
   D. Lung

6. If blood sodium concentration decreases, what is the effect on blood volume?
   A. Increases
   B. Decreases
   C. Remains the same
   D. None of the above

7. Which of the following is true of body water?
   A. It is obtained from the liquids we drink.
   B. It is obtained from the foods we eat.
   C. It is formed by the catabolism of food.
   D. All of the above are true.

8. Edema may result from which of the following?
   A. Retention of electrolytes
   B. Decreased blood pressure
   C. Increased concentration of blood plasma proteins
   D. All of the above

9. The most abundant and most important positive plasma ion is which of the following?
   A. Sodium
   B. Chloride
   C. Calcium
   D. Oxygen

10. Which of the following is true when extracellular fluid volume decreases?
    A. Aldosterone secretion increases.
    B. Kidney tubule reabsorption of sodium increases.
    C. Urine volume decreases.
    D. All of the above are true.

Completion

Choose from the words below to complete the following statements. Write the corresponding letter in the answer blank.

A. Aldosterone
B. Edema
C. Proteins
D. Decreases
E. Diuretic
F. Electrolytes
G. Positive
H. Antidiuretic hormone
I. Dehydration
J. Extracellular fluid
K. Plasma
L. Urine
M. Interstitial fluid
N. Fluid balance

11. Any drug that promotes or stimulates the production of urine is called a _____.

12. The presence of abnormally large amounts of fluid in the intercellular tissue spaces of the body is called _____.

13. Water located outside of cells is called _____. It can be divided into two categories. If located in the spaces between the cells, it is called _____; and if located in blood vessels, it is called _____.

14. Compounds such as sodium chloride that form ions when placed in solution are called _____.

15. When the adrenal cortex increases its secretion of aldosterone, urine volume _____.

16. Most fluids leave the body in the form of _____.

17. When fluid output is greater than fluid intake, _____ occurs.

18. How much water moves into blood from interstitial fluid depends largely on the concentration of _____ present in blood plasma. These substances act as a water-pulling or water-holding force.

19. Urine volume is regulated primarily by a hormone secreted by the posterior lobe of the pituitary gland called _____ and by a hormone secreted by the adrenal gland called _____.

20. Homeostasis of fluids is also known as _____.

CHAPTER 21

Acid-Base Balance

I t has been established in previous chapters that equilibrium between intracellular and extracellular fluid volume must exist for homeostasis to be maintained. Equally important to homeostasis is the chemical acid-base balance of the body fluids. The degree of acidity or alkalinity of a body fluid is expressed in pH value. The neutral point, where a fluid would be neither acid nor alkaline, is pH 7. Increasing acidity is expressed as less than 7, and increasing alkalinity as greater than 7. Examples of body fluids that are acidic are gastric juice (1.6) and urine (6.0). Blood, on the other hand, is considered alkaline with a pH of 7.45.

Buffers are substances that prevent a sharp change in the pH of a fluid when an acid or base is added to it. Buffers are just one of several mechanisms that constantly monitor the pH of fluids in the body. If, for any reason, these mechanisms do not function properly, a pH imbalance occurs. The two general types of imbalances are known as *alkalosis* and *acidosis*.

Maintaining the acid-base balance of body fluids is a matter of vital importance. If this balance varies even slightly, necessary chemical and cellular reactions cannot occur. Your review of this chapter is necessary to understand the delicate acid-base balance that is necessary for survival.

TOPICS FOR REVIEW

Before progressing to Chapter 22, you should have an understanding of the pH of body fluids and the mechanisms that control the pH of these fluids in the body. Your study should conclude with a review of the metabolic and respiratory types of pH imbalances.

pH OF THE BODY

Identify each of the circumstances or substances as acid or base. Write the corresponding letter in the answer blank.

A. Acid   B.   Base

_____ 1.   Lower concentration of hydrogen ions than hydroxide ions
_____ 2.   Higher concentration of hydrogen ions than hydroxide ions
_____ 3.   Gastric juice
_____ 4.   Saliva
_____ 5.   Arterial blood
_____ 6.   Venous blood
_____ 7.   Baking soda
_____ 8.   Beer
_____ 9.   Ammonia
_____ 10. Sea water

▶ *If you had difficulty with this section, review pages 587-588.*

MECHANISMS THAT CONTROL THE pH OF BODY FLUIDS

Circle the correct answer.

11. When carbon dioxide enters the blood, it reacts with the enzyme carbonic anhydrase to form:
    A. Sodium bicarbonate
    B. Water and carbon dioxide
    C. Ammonium chloride
    D. Bicarbonate ion
    E. Carbonic acid

12. The lungs remove _____ liters of carbonic acid each day.
    A. 10.0
    B. 15.0
    C. 20.0
    D. 25.0
    E. 30.0

13. When a buffer reacts with a strong acid, it changes the strong acid to a:
    A. Weak acid
    B. Strong base
    C. Weak base
    D. Water
    E. None of the above

14. Which one of the following is *not* a change in the blood that results from the buffering of fixed acids in tissue capillaries?
    A. The amount of carbonic acid increases slightly.
    B. The amount of bicarbonate in blood decreases.
    C. The hydrogen ion concentration of blood increases slightly.
    D. The blood pH decreases slightly.
    E. All of the above are changes that result from the buffering of fixed acids in tissue capillaries.

15. The most abundant acid in body fluids is:
    A. HCl
    B. Lactic acid
    C. Carbonic acid
    D. Acetic acid
    E. Sulfuric acid

16. The normal ratio of sodium bicarbonate to carbonic acid in arterial blood is:
    A. 5:1
    B. 10:1
    C. 15:1
    D. 20:1
    E. None of the above

17. Which of the following would *not* be a consequence of holding your breath?
    A. The amount of carbonic acid in the blood would increase.
    B. The blood pH would decrease.
    C. The body would develop an alkalosis.
    D. No carbon dioxide could leave the body.

18. The most effective regulators of blood pH are:
    A. The lungs
    B. The kidneys
    C. Buffers
    D. None of the above

19. The pH of the urine may be as low as:
    A. 1.6
    B. 2.5
    C. 3.2
    D. 4.8
    E. 7.4

20. In the distal tubule cells, the product of the reaction aided by carbonic anhydrase is:
    A. Water
    B. Carbon dioxide
    C. Water and carbon dioxide
    D. Hydrogen ions
    E. Carbonic acid

21. In the distal tubule, _____ leaves the tubule cells and enters the blood capillaries.
    A. Carbon dioxide
    B. Water
    C. HCO_3
    D. NaH_2PO_4
    E. $NaHCO_3$

If the statement is true, write "T" in the answer blank. If the statement is false, correct the statement by circling the incorrect term and writing the correct term in the answer blank.

_____ 22. The body has three mechanisms for regulating the pH of its fluids. They are the heart mechanism, the respiratory mechanism, and the urinary mechanism.

_____ 23. Buffers consist of two kinds of substances and therefore are often called *duobuffers*.

_____ 24. Black coffee and cola are acidic on the pH scale.

_____ 25. Some athletes have adopted a technique called *bicarbonate loading*, ingesting large amounts of sodium bicarbonate ($NaHCO_3$) to counteract the effects of lactic acid buildup.

_____ 26. Anything that causes an excessive increase in respiration will, in time, produce acidosis.

_____ 27. Venous blood has a higher pH than arterial blood.

_____ 28. More acids than bases are usually excreted by the kidneys because more acids than bases usually enter the blood.

_____ 29. Blood levels of sodium bicarbonate can be regulated by the lungs.

_____ 30. Blood levels of carbonic acid can be regulated by the kidneys.

▶ *If you had difficulty with this section, review pages 588-594.*

METABOLIC AND RESPIRATORY DISTURBANCES

Match each numbered circumstance with its resulting condition. Write the corresponding letter in the answer blank.

_____ 31. Vomiting

_____ 32. Result of untreated diabetes

_____ 33. Chloride-containing solution

_____ 34. Bicarbonate deficit

_____ 35. Occurs during emesis and may result in metabolic alkalosis

_____ 36. Bicarbonate excess

_____ 37. Rapid breathing

_____ 38. Carbonic acid excess

_____ 39. Carbonic acid deficit

_____ 40. Glucophage

A. Metabolic acidosis

B. Metabolic alkalosis

C. Respiratory acidosis

D. Respiratory alkalosis

E. Emesis

F. Normal saline

G. Uncompensated metabolic acidosis

H. Hyperventilation

I. HCl loss

J. Antidiabetic medication

▶ *If you had difficulty with this section, review pages 594-597.*

APPLYING WHAT YOU KNOW

41. Holly was pregnant and experienced repeated vomiting episodes throughout the day for several days in a row. Her doctor became concerned, admitted her to the hospital, and began intravenous administrations of normal saline. How will this help Holly?

42. Cara had a minor bladder infection. She had heard that this is often the result of the urine being less acidic than necessary and that she should drink cranberry juice to correct the acid problem. She had no cranberry juice, so she decided to substitute orange juice. Why would this substitution not be effective in correcting the acid problem?

43. Mr. Shearer has frequent bouts of hyperacidity of the stomach. Which will assist in neutralizing the acid more promptly: milk or milk of magnesia?

44. Word Find

Find and circle 18 terms presented in this chapter. Words may be spelled top to bottom, bottom to top, right to left, left to right, or diagonally.

```
S  I  S  A  T  S  O  E  M  O  H  P  R  G
E  C  N  A  L  A  B  D  I  U  L  F  E  F
T  S  Y  E  N  D  I  K  W  T  I  K  A  J
Y  D  M  N  D  E  J  W  L  P  T  D  J  I
L  D  N  O  L  H  V  W  O  U  H  D  O  I
O  V  E  R  H  Y  D  R  A  T  I  O  N  S
R  E  I  E  E  D  E  M  A  U  R  O  R  Q
T  L  M  T  C  R  U  L  R  F  S  E  O  Y
C  C  U  S  Z  A  W  E  K  A  T  N  I  X
E  O  Z  O  T  T  A  N  A  U  N  M  F
L  F  K  D  P  I  O  I  W  W  Q  L  G  Q
E  N  I  L  C  O  O  H  O  W  S  B  X  S
N  J  X  A  L  N  F  S  U  N  L  J  J  J
O  C  U  V  S  A  L  G  T  I  S  C  Z  X
N  I  Z  L  L  D  Y  X  Q  Q  K  D  C  D
```

ADH	Edema	Nonelectrolytes
Aldosterone	Electrolytes	Output
Anions	Fluid balance	Overhydration
Cations	Homeostasis	Sodium
Dehydration	Intake	Thirst
Diuretic	Kidneys	Water

DID YOU KNOW?

During the 19th century, English ships that were at sea for many months at a time carried limes onboard to feed the sailors to protect them from developing scurvy. American ships carried cranberries for this purpose.

ACID/BASE BALANCE

Fill in the crossword puzzle.

ACROSS

1. Substance with a pH lower than 7.0
2. Acid-base imbalance
6. Results from the excessive metabolism of fats in uncontrolled diabetics (two words)
7. Vomitus

DOWN

1. Substance with a pH higher than 7.0
2. Serious complication of vomiting
3. Emetic
4. Prevents a sharp change in the pH of fluids
5. Released as a waste product from working muscles (two words)

CHECK YOUR KNOWLEDGE

Multiple Choice

Circle the correct answer.

1. What happens as blood flows through lung capillaries?
   A. Carbonic acid in blood decreases.
   B. Hydrogen ions in blood decrease.
   C. Blood pH increases from venous to arterial blood.
   D. All of the above are true.

2. Which of the following organs is considered the most effective regulator of blood carbonic acid levels?
   A. Kidneys
   B. Intestines
   C. Lungs
   D. Stomach

3. Which of the following organs is considered the most effective regulator of blood pH?
   A. Kidneys
   B. Intestines
   C. Lungs
   D. Stomach

4. What is the pH of the blood?
   A. 7.00 to 8.00
   B. 6 25 to 7.45
   C. 7.65 to 7.85
   D. 7.35 to 7.45

5. If the ratio of sodium bicarbonate to carbonate ions is lowered (perhaps 10 to 1) and blood pH is also lowered, what is the condition called?
   A. Uncompensated metabolic acidosis
   B. Uncompensated metabolic alkalosis
   C. Compensated metabolic acidosis
   D. Compensated metabolic alkalosis

6. If a person hyperventilates for an extended time, which of the following will probably develop?
   A. Metabolic acidosis
   B. Metabolic alkalosis
   C. Respiratory acidosis
   D. Respiratory alkalosis

7. What happens when lactic acid dissociates in the blood?
   A. H+ is added to blood.
   B. pH is lowered.
   C. Acidosis results.
   D. All of the above happen.

8. Which of the following is true of metabolic alkalosis?
   A. It occurs in the case of prolonged vomiting.
   B. It results when the bicarbonate ion is present in excess.
   C. Therapy includes intravenous administration of normal saline.
   D. All of the above are true.

9. Which of the following is a characteristic of a buffer system in the body?
   A. It prevents drastic changes from occurring in body pH.
   B. It picks up both hydrogen and hydroxide ions.
   C. It is exemplified by the bicarbonate-carbonic acid system.
   D. All of the above are true.

10. In the presence of a strong acid (HCl), which of the following is true?
    A. Sodium bicarbonate will react to produce carbonic acid + sodium chloride.
    B. Sodium bicarbonate will react to produce more sodium bicarbonate.
    C. Carbonic acid will react to produce sodium bicarbonate.
    D. Carbonic acid will react to form more carbonic acid.

Matching

Match each description in column A with its corresponding term in column B. (Only one answer is correct for each.)

Column A

_____ 11. pH lower than 7.0

_____ 12. pH higher than 7.0

_____ 13. Prevent sharp pH changes

_____ 14. Decrease in respirations

_____ 15. Increase in respirations

_____ 16. Bicarbonate deficit

_____ 17. Bicarbonate excess

_____ 18. "Fixed" acid

_____ 19. Enzyme found in red blood cells

_____ 20. Lower-than-normal ratio of sodium bicarbonate to carbonic acid

Column B

A. Metabolic acidosis

B. Metabolic alkalosis

C. Alkaline solution

D. Lactic acid

E. Respiratory acidosis

F. Respiratory alkalosis

G. Acidic solution

H. Uncompensated metabolic acidosis

I. Buffers

J. Carbonic anhydrase

CHAPTER 22

The Reproductive Systems

The reproductive system consists of those organs that participate in perpetuating the species. It is a unique body system in that its organs differ between the two sexes, and yet the goal of creating a new being is the same for each gender. Of interest also is the fact that this system is the only one not necessary to the survival of the individual, and yet survival of the species depends on the proper functioning of the reproductive organs.

The male reproductive system is divided into the external genitals, the testes, the duct system, and accessory glands. The testes, or gonads, are considered essential organs because they produce the sex cells, sperm, which join with the female sex cells, ova, to form a new human being. They also secrete the male sex hormone, testosterone, which is responsible for the physical transformation of a boy to a man. Sperm are formed in the testes by the seminiferous tubules. From there they enter a long narrow duct, the epididymis. They continue onward through the vas deferens into the ejaculatory duct, down the urethra, and out of the body. Throughout this journey, various glands secrete substances that add motility to the sperm and create a chemical environment conducive to reproduction.

The female reproductive system is truly extraordinary and diverse. It produces ova, receives the penis and sperm during intercourse, is the site of conception, houses and nourishes the embryo during prenatal development, and nourishes the infant after birth. Because of its diversity, the physiology of the female is generally considered to be more complex than that of the male. Much of the activity of this system revolves around the menstrual cycle and the monthly preparation that the female undergoes for a possible pregnancy.

The organs of the reproductive systems are divided into essential organs and accessory organs of reproduction. The essential organs of the female are the ovaries. Just as with the male, the essential organs of the female are referred to as the *gonads*. The gonads of both sexes produce the sex cells. In the male, the gonads produce the sperm and in the female they produce the ova. The gonads are also responsible for producing the hormones in each gender that are necessary for development of the secondary sex characteristics.

The menstrual cycle of the female typically covers a period of 28 days. Each cycle consists of three phases: the menstrual period, the proliferative phase, and the secretory phase. Changes in the blood levels of the hormones that are responsible for the menstrual cycle also cause physical and emotional changes in the female. Knowledge of these phenomena and this system, in both the male and the female, are necessary to complete your understanding of the reproductive system.

TOPICS FOR REVIEW

Before progressing to Chapter 23, you should familiarize yourself with the structure and function of the organs of the male and female reproductive systems. Your review should include emphasis on the gross and microscopic structure of the testes and the production of sperm and testosterone. Your study should continue by tracing the pathway of a sperm cell from formation to expulsion from the body.

You should then familiarize yourself with the structure and function of the organs of the female reproductive system. Your review should include emphasis on the development of mature ova from ovarian follicles, and should additionally concentrate on the phases and occurrences in a typical 28-day menstrual cycle. Finally, a review of the common disorders occurring in both male and female reproductive systems is necessary to complete the study of this chapter.

MALE REPRODUCTIVE SYSTEM

STRUCTURAL PLAN

Match each term on the left with its related term on the right. Write the corresponding letter in the answer blank.

Group A

_____	1.	Testes	A. Fertilized ovum
_____	2.	Spermatozoa	B. Accessory organ
_____	3.	Ovum	C. Male sex cell
_____	4.	Penis	D. Gonads
_____	5.	Zygote	E. Gamete

Group B

_____	6.	Testes	A. Cowper gland
_____	7.	Bulbourethral	B. Scrotum
_____	8.	Asexual	C. Essential organ
_____	9.	External genital	D. Single parent
_____	10.	Prostate	E. Accessory organ

▷ *If you had difficulty with this section, review pages 603-605.*

TESTES

Circle the correct answer.

11. The testes are surrounded by a tough membrane called the:
    A. Ductus deferens
    B. Tunica albuginea
    C. Septum
    D. Seminiferous membrane

12. The _____ lie near the septa that separate the lobules.
    A. Ductus deferens
    B. Sperm
    C. Interstitial cells
    D. Nerves

13. Sperm are found in the walls of the _____.
    A. Seminiferous tubule
    B. Interstitial cells
    C. Septum
    D. Blood vessels

14. The scrotum provides an environment that is approximately _____ for the testes.
    A. The same as the body temperature
    B. 5 degrees warmer than the body temperature
    C. 3 degrees warmer than the body temperature
    D. 3 degrees cooler than the body temperature

15. The _____ produce(s) testosterone.
    A. Seminiferous tubules
    B. Prostate gland
    C. Bulbourethral gland
    D. Pituitary gland
    E. Interstitial cells

16. The part of the sperm that contains genetic information that will be inherited is the:
    A. Tail
    B. Neck
    C. Middle piece
    D. Head
    E. Acrosome

17. Which one of the following is *not* a function of testosterone?
    A. It causes a deepening of the voice.
    B. It promotes the development of the male accessory organs.
    C. It has a stimulatory effect on protein catabolism.
    D. It causes greater muscular development and strength.

18. Sperm production is called:
    A. Spermatogonia
    B. Spermatids
    C. Spermatogenesis
    D. Spermatocyte

19. The section of the sperm that contains enzymes that enable it to break down the covering of the ovum and permit entry should contact occur is the:
    A. Acrosome
    B. Midpiece
    C. Tail
    D. Stem

Fill in the blanks.

The (20) _____ are the gonads of the male. From puberty on, the seminiferous tubules are continuously forming (21) _____. Any of these cells may join with the female sex cell, the (22) _____, to become a new human being. Another function of the testes is to secrete the male hormone (23) _____, which transforms a boy to a man. This hormone is secreted by the (24) _____ _____ of the testes. A good way to remember testosterone's functions is to think of it as "the (25) _____ hormone" and "the (26) _____ hormone."

▶ *If you had difficulty with this section, review pages 605-609.*

REPRODUCTIVE DUCTS
ACCESSORY OR SUPPORTIVE SEX GLANDS
EXTERNAL GENITALS

Match each description on the left with its corresponding term on the right. Write the letter in the answer blank.

_____ 27. Continuation of ducts that start in the epididymis

_____ 28. Erectile tissue

_____ 29. Also known as *bulbourethral*

_____ 30. Narrow tube that lies along the top and behind the testes

_____ 31. Doughnut-shaped gland beneath the bladder

_____ 32. Point where ductus (vas) deferens joins the duct from the seminal vesicle

_____ 33. Mixture of sperm and secretions of accessory sex glands

_____ 34. Contributes 60% of the seminal fluid volume

_____ 35. Removed during circumcision

_____ 36. External genitalia

A. Epididymis

B. Ductus (vas) deferens

C. Ejaculatory duct

D. Prepuce

E. Seminal vesicles

F. Prostate gland

G. Cowper gland

H. Corpus spongiosum

I. Semen

J. Scrotum

▶ *If you had difficulty with this section, review pages 609-611.*

DISORDERS OF THE MALE REPRODUCTIVE SYSTEM

Fill in the blanks.

37. Decreased sperm production is called _____.

38. Testes normally descend into the scrotum about _____ _____ before birth.

39. If a baby is born with undescended testes, a condition called _____ results.

40. A common noncancerous condition of the prostate in older men is known as

_____ _____

_____.

41. _____ is a condition in which the foreskin fits so tightly over the glans that it cannot retract.

42. Failure to achieve an erection of the penis is called _____.

43. An accumulation of fluid in the scrotum is known as a _____.

44. An _____ _____ results when the intestines push through the weak area of the abdominal wall, which separates the abdominopelvic cavity from the scrotum.

45. The PSA test is a screening test for cancer of the _____.

▶ *If you had difficulty with this section, review pages 611-614.*

FEMALE REPRODUCTIVE SYSTEM
STRUCTURAL PLAN

Match the term on the left with the corresponding term on the right. Write the letter in the answer blank.

_____ 46. Ovaries   A. Genitals

_____ 47. Vagina   B. Accessory sex gland

_____ 48. Bartholin   C. Accessory duct

_____ 49. Vulva   D. Gonads

_____ 50. Ova   E. Sex cell

Identify each of the numbered structures as external or internal. Write the corresponding letter in the answer blank.

A. External structure   B. Internal structure

_____ 51. Mons pubis

_____ 52. Vagina

_____ 53. Labia majora

_____ 54. Uterine tubes

_____ 55. Vestibule

_____ 56. Clitoris

_____ 57. Labia minora

_____ 58. Ovaries

▶ *If you had difficulty with this section, review pages 614-617.*

OVARIES

Fill in the blanks.

The ovaries are the (59) _____ of the female. They have two main functions. The first is the production of the female sex cell. This process is called
(60) _____. The specialized type of cell division that occurs during sexual
cell reproduction is known as (61) _____. The ovum is the body's largest
cell and has (62) _____ the number of chromosomes found in other body
cells. At the time of (63) _____, the sex cells from both parents fuse and
(64) _____ chromosomes are united. The second major function of the ovaries is to secrete the sex hormones (65) _____ and
(66) _____. Estrogen is the sex hormone that causes the development and
maintenance of the female (67) _____
_____ _____. Progesterone acts with estrogen to help initiate the (68) _____
_____ in girls entering (69) _____.

▶ *If you had difficulty with this section, review pages 614-617.*

FEMALE REPRODUCTIVE DUCTS

Match each of the numbered descriptions with its corresponding structure. Write the letter in the answer blank.

A. Uterine tubes   B. Uterus   C. Vagina

_____ 70.   Location of most ectopic pregnancies

_____ 71.   Lining known as *endometrium*

_____ 72.   Birth canal

_____ 73.   Site of menstruation

_____ 74.   Fringelike projections called *fimbriae*

_____ 75.   Consists of a body, fundus, and cervix

_____ 76.   Site of fertilization

_____ 77.   Also known as *oviduct*

_____ 78.   Entranceway for sperm

▶ *If you had difficulty with this section, review pages 617-618.*

ACCESSORY OR SUPPORTIVE SEX GLANDS
EXTERNAL GENITALS

Match each term on the left with its corresponding description on the right. Write the letter in the answer blank.

Group A

_____ 79.   Bartholin glands   A.   Colored area around the nipple

_____ 80.   Breasts   B.   Grapelike clusters of milk-secreting cells

_____ 81.   Alveoli   C.   Drain alveoli

_____ 82.   Lactiferous ducts   D.   Also known as *greater vestibular*

_____ 83.   Areola   E.   Composed primarily of fat tissue

Group B

_____ 84.   Mons pubis   A.   "Large lips"

_____ 85.   Labia majora   B.   Area between the vaginal opening and the anus

_____ 86.   Clitoris   C.   Surgical procedure

_____ 87.   Perineum   D.   Composed of erectile tissue

_____ 88.   Episiotomy   E.   Pad of fat over the symphysis pubis

▶ *If you had difficulty with this section, review pages 618-620.*

MENSTRUAL CYCLE

If the statement is true, write "T" in the answer blank. If the statement is false, correct the statement by circling the incorrect term and writing the correct term in the answer blank.

_____ 89. *Climacteric* is the scientific name for the beginning of the menses.

_____ 90. As a general rule, several ovum mature each month during the 30 to 40 years that a woman has menstrual periods.

_____ 91. Ovulation occurs 28 days before the next menstrual period begins.

_____ 92. The first day of ovulation is considered the first day of the cycle.

_____ 93. A woman's fertile period lasts only a few days out of each month.

_____ 94. The control of the menstrual cycle lies in the posterior pituitary gland.

Match the two hormones below to their corresponding descriptions. Write the letter in the answer blank.

A. FSH   B. LH

_____ 95. Ovulating hormone

_____ 96. Secreted during first days of menstrual cycle

_____ 97. Secreted after estrogen level of blood increases

_____ 98. Causes final maturation of follicle and ovum

_____ 99. Suppressed by birth control pills

▶ *If you had difficulty with this section, review pages 620-622.*

DISORDERS OF THE FEMALE REPRODUCTIVE SYSTEM

Match each numbered description to its corresponding disease or condition. Write the letter in the answer blank.

_____ 100. Often occurs as a result of an STD or a "yeast infection"

_____ 101. Benign tumor of smooth muscle and fibrous connective tissue; also known as a *fibroid tumor*

_____ 102. Yeast infection characterized by leukorrhea

_____ 103. Inflammation of an ovary

_____ 104. Benign lumps in one or both breasts

_____ 105. Venereal diseases

_____ 106. Results from pathogenic organisms transmitted from another person; for example, an STD

_____ 107. Painful menstruation

_____ 108. Asymptomatic in most women and nearly all men

_____ 109. Results from a hormonal imbalance rather than from an infection or disease condition

_____ 110. Screening test for cervical cancer

_____ 111. Causes blisters on the skin of the genitals; the blisters may disappear temporarily, but recur, especially as a result of stress

A. Candidiasis

B. Dysmenorrhea

C. Exogenous infections
D. DUB
E. Myoma
F. Vaginitis
G. Sexually transmitted diseases (STDs)
H. Oophoritis
I. Fibrocystic disease
J. Pap smear

K. Genital herpes
L. Trichomoniasis

▶ *If you had difficulty with this section, review pages 622-629.*

APPLYING WHAT YOU KNOW

112. Sam is going into the hospital for the surgical removal of his testes. As a result of this surgery, will Sam be impotent?

113. When baby Christopher was born, the pediatrician, Dr. Self, discovered that his left testicle had not descended into the scrotum. If this situation is not corrected soon, might baby Christopher be sterile or impotent?

114. Charlene contracted gonorrhea. By the time she made an appointment to see her doctor, it had spread to her abdominal organs. How is this possible when gonorrhea is a disease of the reproductive system?

115. Dr. Sullivan advised Mrs. Harlan to have a bilateral oophorectomy. Is this a sterilization procedure? Will she experience menopause?

116. Vicki had a total hysterectomy. Will she experience menopause?

117. Word Find

Find and circle 18 terms presented in this chapter. Words may be spelled top to bottom, bottom to top, right to left, left to right, or diagonally.

```
M K O V I D U C T S E D H G
S E I R A V O I F U T G L L
I N H Z H M P M K O H I C W
D D V A S D E F E R E N S H
I O A C C I P J V E H Y D S
H M G R R B M N X F G Y I O
C E I O O E Z Y T I C S T E
R T N S T P S D D N O V A D
O R A O U W E B A I J S M Z
T I C M M E Y N E M D L R V
P U A E U D G M I E H I E H
Y M O T C E T A T S O R P B
R P E E R M N E G O R T S E
C O W P E R S I N X K E A P
```

Acrosome	Meiosis	Scrotum
Cowpers	Ovaries	Seminiferous
Cryptorchidism	Oviducts	Sperm
Endometrium	Penis	Spermatids
Epididymis	Pregnancy	Vagina
Estrogen	Prostatectomy	Vas deferens

DID YOU KNOW?

The testes produce approximately 50 million sperm per day. Every 2 to 3 months they produce enough cells to populate the entire earth.

There are an estimated 925,000 daily occurrences of STD transmission and 550,000 daily conceptions world-wide.

The United States has one of the highest teen pregnancy rates of all industrialized nations. Rates in France, Germany, and Japan are four times lower.

REPRODUCTIVE SYSTEM

Fill in the crossword puzzle.

ACROSS

2. Female erectile tissue
3. Colored area around nipple
5. Male reproductive fluid
6. Sex cells
7. External genitalia
10. Male sex hormone

DOWN

1. Failure to have a menstrual period
2. Surgical removal of foreskin
4. Foreskin
8. Menstrual period
9. Essential organs of reproduction

CHECK YOUR KNOWLEDGE

Multiple Choice

Circle the correct answer.

1. What is the membrane that may cover the vaginal opening of the female called?
   A. Hymen
   B. Mons pubis
   C. Labia
   D. Clitoris

2. Which of the following statements is/are true of the menstrual cycle?
   A. Estrogen levels are lowest at the time of ovulation.
   B. Progesterone levels are highest at the time of ovulation.
   C. FSH levels are highest during the proliferation phase.
   D. None of the above are true.

3. A fluid mixture called *semen* could contain which of the following?
   A. Sperm cells
   B. Secretion from the prostate
   C. Secretions from the seminal vesicles
   D. All of the above

4. What is the failure of the testes to descend into the scrotum before birth called?
   A. Cryptococcus
   B. Coccidiomycosis
   C. Cryptorchidism
   D. Cholelithiasis

5. Which of the following is *not* an accessory organ of the female reproductive system?
   A. Breast
   B. Bartholin glands
   C. Ovary
   D. All of the above are accessory organs

6. Which of the following structures can be referred to as *male gonads*?
   A. Testes
   B. Epididymis
   C. Vas deferens
   D. All of the above

7. Sperm cells are suspended outside the body cavity so as to do which of the following?
   A. Protect them from trauma
   B. Keep them at a cooler temperature
   C. Keep them supplied with a greater number of blood vessels
   D. Protect them from infection

8. Surgical removal of the foreskin from the glans penis is called what?
   A. Vasectomy
   B. Sterilization
   C. Circumcision
   D. Ligation

9. What is the colored area around the nipple of the breast called?
   A. Areola
   B. Lactiferous duct
   C. Alveoli
   D. None of the above

10. The female organ that is analogous to the penis in the male is the:
    A. Labia minora
    B. Labia majora.
    C. Vulva.
    D. Clitoris.

Completion

Complete the following statements using the terms listed below. Write the corresponding letter in the answer blank.

A. Clitoris

B. Endometrium

C. Ectopic

D. Corpus luteum

E. Menses

F. Epididymis

G. Hysterectomy

H. Prostate

I. FSH (follicle-stimulating hormone)

J. Ovulation

K. Scrotum

L. Testosterone

11. A pregnancy resulting from the implantation of a fertilized ovum in any location other than the uterus is called _____.

12. Interstitial cells of the testes function to produce _____.

13. The doughnut-shaped accessory organ or gland that surrounds the male urethra is called the _____.

14. Surgical removal of the uterus is called _____.

15. The _____ houses sperm cells as they mature and develop their ability to swim.

16. The skin-covered, external pouch that contains the testes is called the _____.

17. The lining of the uterus is called _____.

18. The hormone progesterone is secreted by a structure called the _____.

19. Fertilization of an egg by a sperm can only occur around the time of _____.

20. From about the first to the seventh day of the menstrual cycle, the anterior pituitary gland secretes _____.

MALE REPRODUCTIVE ORGANS

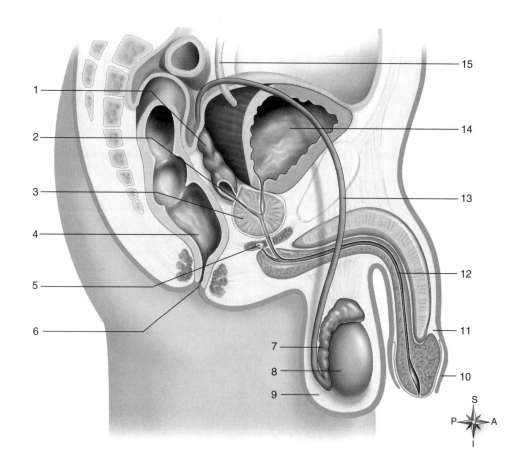

1. _____

2. _____

3. _____

4. _____

5. _____

6. _____

7. _____

8. _____

9. _____

10. _____

11. _____

12. _____

13. _____

14. _____

15. _____

TUBULES OF TESTIS AND EPIDIDYMIS

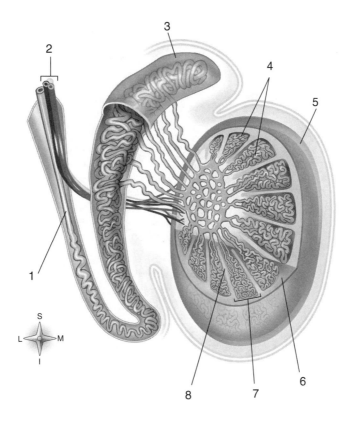

1. _____

2. _____

3. _____

4. _____

5. _____

6. _____

7. _____

8. _____

VULVA

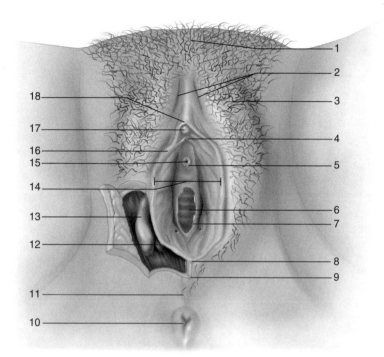

1. _____

2. _____

3. _____

4. _____

5. _____

6. _____

7. _____

8. _____

9. _____

10. _____

11. _____

12. _____

13. _____

14. _____

15. _____

16. _____

17. _____

18. _____

BREAST

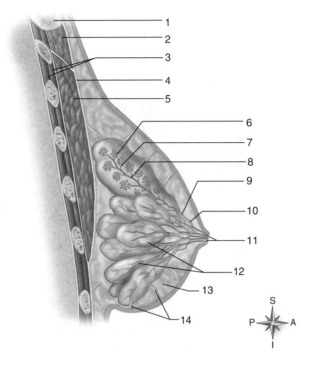

1. _____

2. _____

3. _____

4. _____

5. _____

6. _____

7. _____

8. _____

9. _____

10. _____

11. _____

12. _____

13. _____

14. _____

FEMALE PELVIS

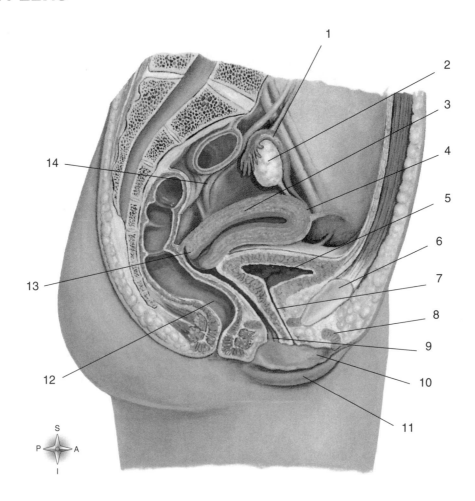

1. _____   8. _____

2. _____   9. _____

3. _____   10. _____

4. _____   11. _____

5. _____   12. _____

6. _____   13. _____

7. _____   14. _____

UTERUS AND ADJACENT STRUCTURES

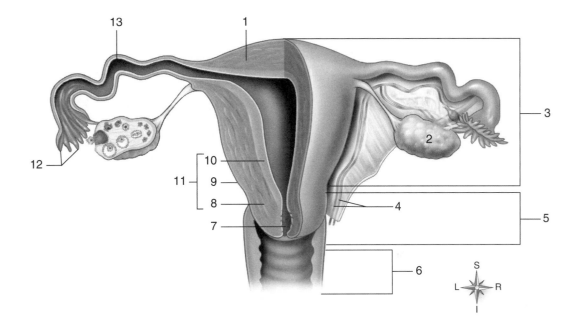

1. _____

2. _____

3. _____

4. _____

5. _____

6. _____

7. _____

8. _____

9. _____

10. _____

11. _____

12. _____

13. _____

CHAPTER 23

Growth and Development

Millions of fragile microscopic sperm swim against numerous obstacles to reach an ovum and create a new life. At birth, the newborn will fill his lungs with air and cry lustily, signaling to the world that he is ready to begin the cycle of life. This cycle will be marked by ongoing changes, periodic physical growth, and continuous development.

This chapter reviews the more significant events that occur in the normal growth and development of an individual from conception to death. Realizing that each person is unique, we nonetheless can discover amid all the complexities of humanity some constants that are understandable and predictable.

Knowledge of human growth and development is essential in understanding the commonalties that influence individuals as they pass through the cycle of life.

TOPICS FOR REVIEW

Before progressing to Chapter 24, you should have an understanding of the concept of development as a biological process. You should familiarize yourself with the major developmental changes from conception through older adulthood. The disorders of pregnancy should be emphasized as you review the chapter. Finally, your study should conclude with a review of the effects of aging on the body systems.

PRENATAL PERIOD
BIRTH OR PARTURITION

Fill in the blanks.

The prenatal stage of development begins at the time of

(1) _____ and continues until

(2) _____. The science of the development of an individual before birth is called (3) _____. Fertilization

takes place in the outer third of the (4) _____. The

fertilized ovum or (5) _____ begins to divide and in

approximately 3 days forms a solid mass called a

(6) _____. By the time it enters the uterus, it is a hollow ball of cells called a (7) _____. As it continues to

develop, it forms a structure with two cavities. The (8) _____

_____ will become a fluid-filled sac for the embryo. The

(9) _____ will develop into an important fetal membrane in the

(10) _____.

Match each description on the left with its corresponding term on the right. Write the letter in the answer blank.

_____ 11. "Within a glass"   A. Laparoscope

_____ 12. Inside germ layer   B. Gestation

_____ 13. Before birth   C. Antenatal

_____ 14. Length of pregnancy   D. Histogenesis

_____ 15. Fiber optic viewing instrument   E. Apgar score

_____ 16. Process of birth   F. Endoderm

_____ 17. System used to assess the general condition of a   G. In vitro
           newborn

_____ 18. Study of how the primary germ layers develop into   H. Parturition
           many different kinds of tissues

_____ 19. Term used to describe the developing individual in   I. Embryo
           the first trimester of pregnancy

_____ 20. Monitors progress of developing fetus   J. Ultrasonogram

▶ *If you had difficulty with this section, review pages 639-650.*

DISORDERS OF PREGNANCY

If the statement is true, write "T" in the answer blank. If the statement is false, correct the statement by circling the incorrect term and writing the correct term in the answer blank.

_____ 21. Many offspring are lost before implantation occurs, often for unknown reasons.

_____ 22. The most common type of ectopic pregnancy is a tubal pregnancy.

_____ 23. If the placenta grows too closely to the cervical opening, a condition called *abruptio placentae* results.

_____ 24. Separation of the placenta from the uterine wall in a pregnancy of 20 weeks or more is known as *placenta previa*.

_____ 25. Toxemia of pregnancy is also known as *puerperal fever*.

_____ 26. After 20 weeks, delivery of a lifeless infant is termed a *miscarriage*.

_____ 27. Acquired birth defects result from agents called *teratogens* that disrupt normal histogenesis and organogenesis.

▶ *If you had difficulty with this section, review pages 649-651.*

POSTNATAL PERIOD

Circle the correct answer.

28. During the postnatal period:
    A. The head becomes proportionately smaller
    B. Thoracic and abdominal contours change from round to elliptical
    C. The legs become proportionately longer
    D. The trunk becomes proportionately shorter
    E. All of the above take place during the postnatal period

29. The period of infancy starts at birth and lasts about:
    A. 4 weeks
    B. 4 months
    C. 10 weeks
    D. 12 months
    E. 18 months

30. The lumbar curvature of the spine appears _____ months after birth.
    A. 1 to 10
    B. 5 to 8
    C. 8 to 12
    D. 11 to 15
    E. 12 to 18

31. During the first 4 months, the birth weight will:
    A. Double
    B. Triple
    C. Quadruple
    D. None of the above

32. At the end of the first year, the weight of the baby will have:
    A. Doubled
    B. Tripled
    C. Quadrupled
    D. None of the above

33. The infant is capable of following a moving object with its eyes at:
    A. 2 days
    B. 2 weeks
    C. 2 months
    D. 4 months
    E. 10 months

34. The infant can lift its head and raise its chest at:
    A. 2 months
    B. 3 months
    C. 4 months
    D. 10 months

35. The infant can crawl at:
    A. 2 months
    B. 3 months
    C. 4 months
    D. 10 months
    E. 12 months

36. The infant can stand alone at:
    A. 2 months
    B. 3 months
    C. 4 months
    D. 10 months
    E. 12 months

37. The permanent teeth, with the exception of the third molar, have all erupted by the age of _____ years.
    A. 6
    B. 8
    C. 12
    D. 14
    E. None of the above

38. Puberty starts at age _____ years in boys.
    A. 10 to 13
    B. 12 to 14
    C. 14 to 16
    D. None of the above

39. Most girls begin breast development at about age:
    A. 8
    B. 9
    C. 10
    D. 11
    E. 12

40. The growth spurt is generally complete by age _____ in males.
    A. 14
    B. 15
    C. 16
    D. 18

41. An average age at which girls begin to menstruate is _____ years.
    A. 10 to 12
    B. 11 to 12
    C. 12 to 13
    D. 13 to 14
    E. 14 to 15

42. The first sign of puberty in boys is:
    A. Facial hair
    B. Increased muscle mass
    C. Pubic hair
    D. Deepening of the voice
    E. Enlargement of the testicles

Match each description on the left with its corresponding term on the right. Write the letter in the answer blank.

_____ 43. Begins at birth and lasts until death	A. Neonatology
_____ 44. Study of the diagnosis and treatment of disorders of the newborn	B. Neonatal
_____ 45. Teenage years	C. Adolescence
_____ 46. From the end of infancy to puberty	D. Deciduous
_____ 47. Baby teeth	E. Puberty
_____ 48. First 4 weeks of infancy	F. Postnatal
_____ 49. Age at which secondary sexual characteristics occur	G. Gerontology
_____ 50. Study of aging	H. Childhood
_____ 51. Older adulthood	I. Senescence

▶ *If you had difficulty with this section, review pages 651-656.*

EFFECTS OF AGING

Fill in the blanks.

52. Old bones develop indistinct and shaggy margins with spurs; a process called
    _____.

53. A degenerative joint disease common in the aged is _____.

54. The number of _____ units in the kidney decreases by almost 50% between the ages of 30 and 75.

55. In old age, respiratory efficiency decreases and a condition known as
    _____ _____ results.

56. Fatty deposits accumulate in blood vessels as we age, and the result is
    _____, which narrows the passageway for the flow of blood.

57. Hardening of the arteries, or _____, occurs during the aging process.

58. Another term for high blood pressure is _____.

59. Hardening of the lens is _____.

60. If the lens becomes cloudy and impairs vision, it is called a _____.

61. _____ causes an increase in the pressure within the eyeball and may result in blindness.

▶ *If you had difficulty with this section, review pages 656-659.*

UNSCRAMBLE THE WORDS

62. **A N N F C Y I**

   ⬭   ⬭   ☐   ☐   ☐   ☐

63. **N A A L T T S O P**

   ☐ ☐ ☐ ☐ ⬭ ☐ ⬭ ☐ ⬭

64. **O G S S N E G R A O N E I**

   ☐ ⬭ ☐ ⬭ ☐ ☐ ☐ ⬭ ☐ ☐ ☐ ⬭ ☐

65. **G T E Y Z O**

   ⬭ ☐ ☐ ⬭ ☐ ☐

66. **H D O O L H C I D**

   ☐ ☐ ⬭ ☐ ☐ ☐ ⬭ ☐ ☐

Take the circled letters, unscramble them, and fill in the solution.

The secret to Farmer Brown's prize pumpkin crop.

67. ☐ ☐ ☐ ☐ ☐ ☐ ☐ ☐ ☐ ☐ ☐ ☐ ☐ ☐

APPLYING WHAT YOU KNOW

68. Billy's mother told the pediatrician during his 1-year visit that Billy had tripled his birth weight, was crawling actively, and could stand alone. Is Billy's development normal, retarded, or advanced?

69. John is 70 years old. He has always enjoyed food and has had a hearty appetite. Lately, however, he has complained that food "just doesn't taste as good anymore." What might be a possible explanation?

70. Mr. Gaylor has noticed hearing problems but only under certain circumstances. He has difficulty with certain tones, especially high or low tones, but has no problem with everyday conversation. What might be a possible explanation?

71. Mrs. Lowell gave birth to twin girls. The obstetrician, Dr. Sullivan, advised Mr. Lowell that even though the girls looked identical, they were really fraternal twins. How was he able to deduce this?

72. Word Find

Find and circle 13 terms presented in this chapter. Words may be spelled top to bottom, bottom to top, right to left, left to right, or diagonally.

```
F C M P O D N P P A G M J N Z
K E C N E C S E L O D A G G M
I N R B U X T K D A Y Q T F R
L D L T O M S D W A E Z B F E
Z O B A I S P M A L C E E R P
W D I M P L A N T A T I O N L
H E N M K A I T E P D K S X A
W R G A S A R Z R N T Q P Y C
L M Q S I J O O A U B F G T E
R T N T B N G E S T A T I O N
L A T I N E G N O C I T F Z T
D C B T R L A S G C O O R R A
E N O I T I R U T R A P N S B
N V A S N N E G O T A R E T E
```

Adolescence   Implantation   Placenta
Congenital   Laparoscope   Preeclampsia
Endoderm   Mastitis   Progeria
Fertilization   Parturition   Teratogen
Gestation

DID YOU KNOW?

Brain cells do not regenerate. One beer permanently destroys 10,000 brain cells.

GROWTH/DEVELOPMENT

Fill in the crossword puzzle.

ACROSS

7. Old age
9. Fatty deposit buildup on walls of arteries
10. Cloudy lens
11. Name of zygote after 3 days
12. Fertilized ovum

DOWN

1. Process of birth
2. Science of the development of the individual before birth
3. Study of how germ layers develop into tissues
4. Name of zygote after implantation
5. First 4 weeks of infancy
6. Hardening of the lens
8. Eye disease marked by increased pressure in the eyeball
10. Will develop into a fetal membrane in the placenta

CHECK YOUR KNOWLEDGE

Multiple Choice

Circle the correct answer.

1. When the human embryo is a hollow ball of cells consisting of an outer cell layer and an inner cell mass, what is it called?
   A. Morula
   B. Chorion
   C. Blastocyst
   D. Zygote

2. Degenerative changes in the urinary system that accompany old age include which of the following?
   A. Decreased capacity of the bladder and the inability to empty or void completely
   B. Decrease in the number of nephrons
   C. Less blood flow through the kidneys
   D. All of the above

3. The frontal and maxillary sinuses of the facial region acquire permanent placement or develop fully when the individual is in a stage of development known as which of the following?
   A. Infancy
   B. Childhood
   C. Adolescence
   D. Adulthood

4. The first 4 weeks of human life following birth are referred to as which of the following?
   A. Neonatal
   B. Infancy
   C. Prenatal
   D. Embryonic

5. Any hardening of the arteries is referred to as which of the following?
   A. Angioma
   B. Atherosclerosis
   C. Angina
   D. Arteriosclerosis

6. Which of the following is characteristic of the disorder called *presbyopia*?
   A. It is very characteristic of old age.
   B. It causes farsightedness in some individuals.
   C. It is characterized by the lens in the eye becoming hard and losing its elasticity.
   D. All of the above are true.

7. The three most important "low tech" methods for improving the quality of life as you age are:
   A. Healthy diet, exercise, and stress management
   B. A healthy diet, marriage, and money
   C. A healthy diet, good job, and living in the suburbs
   D. A healthy diet, weight management, and exercise

8. Which of the following events, if any, is *not* characteristic of adolescence?
   A. Bone closure occurs.
   B. Secondary sexual characteristics develop.
   C. Very rapid growth occurs.
   D. All of the above events are characteristic of adolescence.

9. Which of the following events is *not* characteristic of the prenatal period of development?
   A. Blastocyst is formed.
   B. Histogenesis occurs.
   C. Bone closure occurs.
   D. Amniotic cavity is formed.

10. Which of the following structures is derived from ectoderm?
   A. The lining of the lungs
   B. The brain
   C. The kidneys
   D. All of the above

Matching

Match each term in column A with its corresponding definition in column B. (Only one answer is correct for each.)

Column A

_____ 11. Arteriosclerosis

_____ 12. Atherosclerosis

_____ 13. Parturition

_____ 14. Cataract

_____ 15. Adolescence

_____ 16. Amniotic sac

_____ 17. Glaucoma

_____ 18. Senescence

_____ 19. Hypertension

_____ 20. Placenta

Column B

A. High blood pressure

B. Chorion

C. Birth

D. "Bag of waters"

E. Hardening of arteries

F. Degeneration

G. Fat accumulation in arteries

H. Secondary sexual characteristics

I. Clouding of eye lens

J. High eye pressure

FERTILIZATION AND IMPLANTATION

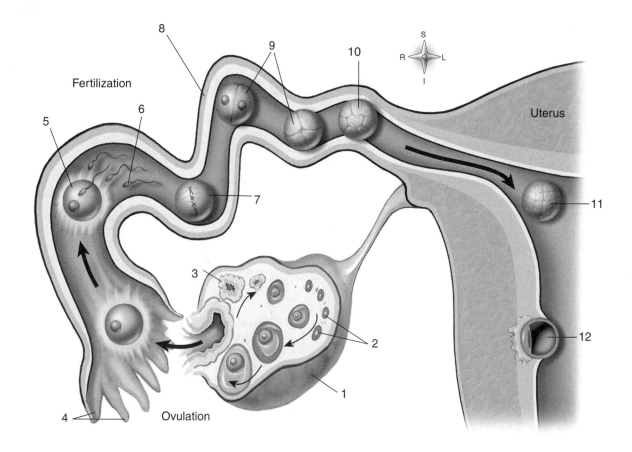

1. _____
2. _____
3. _____
4. _____
5. _____
6. _____

7. _____
8. _____
9. _____
10. _____
11. _____
12. _____

CHAPTER 24

Genetics and Genetic Diseases

L ook around your classroom and you will notice various combinations of hair color, eye color, body size, skin tone, hair texture, gender, etc. Everyone has unique body features and this phenomenon alerts us to the marvel of genetics. Independent units, called *genes*, are responsible for the inheritance of biological traits. Genes determine the structure and function of the human body by producing specific regulatory enzymes. Some genes are dominant and some are recessive. Dominant genes produce traits that appear in the offspring and recessive genes have traits that do not appear in the offspring when they are masked by a dominant gene.

Gene therapy is one of the latest advances of science. This revolutionary branch of medicine combines current technology with genetic research to unlock the secrets of the human body. Daily discoveries in the prevention, diagnosis, treatment, and cure of diseases and disorders are being revealed as a result of genetic therapy. Knowledge of genetics is necessary to understand the basic mechanism by which traits are transmitted from parents to offspring.

TOPICS FOR REVIEW

Your review of this chapter should include an understanding of chromosomes, genes, and gene expression. You should continue your study with a knowledge of common genetic diseases. Finally, your review should conclude with an understanding of the prevention and treatment of genetic diseases.

GENETICS AND HUMAN DISEASE
CHROMOSOMES AND GENES
HUMAN GENOME

Match each term on the left with its corresponding description on the right. Write the letter in the answer blank.

_____ 1. Gene   A.   DNA molecule

_____ 2. Chromosome   B.   Male or female reproductive cell

_____ 3. Gamete   C.   Special form of nuclear division

_____ 4. Meiosis   D.   Formed by union of sperm and ovum at conception

_____ 5. Zygote   E.   Distinct code within a DNA molecule

_____ 6. Genome   F.   Adenine

_____ 7. Genomics   G.   Entire collection of genetic material in each typical cell

_____ 8. Proteomics   H.   Cartoon of a chromosome

_____ 9. Ideogram   I.   Analysis of the genome's code

_____ 10. Nucleotide base   J.   Analysis of the proteins encoded by the genome

▷ *If you had difficulty with this section, review pages 665-669.*

GENE EXPRESSION

Fill in the blanks.

After experimentation with pea plants, Mendel discovered that each inherited trait is controlled by two sets

of similar (11) _____, one from each parent. He also noted that some genes

are (12) _____ and some are (13) _____.

In the example of albinism, a person with the gene combination of Aa is said to be a genetic

(14) _____. If two different dominant genes occur together a form of domi-

nance called (15) _____ exists. (16) _____

chromosomes do not have matching structures. If an individual has the sex chromosomes XX, that person will

have the sexual characteristics of a (17) _____.

(18) _____ simply means "change." A

(19) _____ _____ is a change in the ge-

netic code.

▷ *If you had difficulty with this section, review pages 669-672.*

GENETIC DISEASES

Match each description on the left with its corresponding term on the right. Write the letter in the answer blank.

_____ 20. Caused by recessive genes in chromosome pair 7

_____ 21. Results in total blindness by age 30

_____ 22. Disease conditions that result from the combined effects of inheritance and environmental factors

_____ 23. Results from a failure to produce the enzyme phenylalanine hydroxylase

_____ 24. Presence of only one autosome instead of a pair

_____ 25. Usually caused by trisomy of chromosome 21

_____ 26. Cystic fibrosis is an example

_____ 27. Results from nondisjunction of chromosomes and typically has the XXY pattern

_____ 28. Term used to describe what happens when a pair of chromosomes fails to separate

_____ 29. Sometimes called *XO syndrome*, it is treated with hormone therapy

A. Single-gene disease

B. Nondisjunction

C. Monosomy

D. Leber hereditary optic neuropathy

E. Cystic fibrosis

F. Phenylketonuria

G. Down syndrome

H. Klinefelter syndrome

I. Turner syndrome

J. Genetic predisposition

 If you had difficulty with this section, review pages 672-676.

PREVENTION AND TREATMENT OF GENETIC DISEASES

Circle the correct answer.

30. A pedigree is a chart that can be used to determine:
    A. Genetic relationships in a family over several generations
    B. The possibility of producing offspring with certain genetic disorders
    C. The possibility of a person developing a genetic disorder late in life
    D. All of the above
    E. None of the above

31. The Punnett square is a grid used to determine:
    A. Genetic disorders
    B. The probability of inheriting genetic traits
    C. Proper gene replacement therapy
    D. The necessity for amniocentesis

32. Some forms of cancer are thought to be caused, at least in part, by abnormal genes called:
    A. Cancercytes
    B. Trisomy
    C. Oncogenes
    D. Autosomes

33. When producing a karyotype, the most common source of cells for the sample is the:
    A. Vagina
    B. Rectum
    C. Lining of the cheek
    D. Throat

34. An ultrasound transducer is used during amniocentesis to:
    A. Create a sharper image
    B. Take measurements during the procedure
    C. Prevent damaging rays during the procedure
    D. Guide the tip of the needle to prevent placental damage

35. Electrophoresis is a process that:
    A. Provides a method for DNA analysis
    B. Means electric separation
    C. Is the basis for DNA fingerprinting
    D. All of the above

36. The use of genetic therapy began in 1990 with a group of young children who had:
    A. AIDS
    B. Adenosine deaminase deficiency
    C. Hemophilia
    D. Cystic fibrosis

If the statement is true, write "T" in the answer blank. If the statement is false, correct the statement by circling the incorrect term and writing the correct term in the answer blank.

_____ 37. Chorionic villus sampling is a procedure in which cells that surround a young embryo are collected through the opening of the cervix.

_____ 38. Karyotyping is the process used for DNA fingerprinting.

_____ 39. In amniocentesis, normal genes are introduced with the hope that they will add to the production of the needed protein.

_____ 40. Deficiency of adenosine deaminase results in severe combined immune deficiency.

_____ 41. One hypothesis that may explain some forms of cancer is known as the *tumor suppressor gene* hypothesis.

▶ *If you had difficulty with this section, review pages 676-681.*

UNSCRAMBLE THE WORDS

42. **R C R R I E A**

[ ][ ][○][ ][○][ ][ ]

43. **Y T S M O I R**

[○][ ][○][ ][ ][ ][ ]

44. **E G N E**

[ ][ ][○][ ]

45. **D P E R E G I E**

[ ][ ][○][○][ ][ ][ ][ ]

46. **S O E M C R O S H O M**

[ ][○][ ][ ][ ][ ][ ][ ][ ][○][ ]

Take the circled letters, unscramble them, and fill in the solution.

How Bill made his fortune.

47. [ ][ ][ ][ ][ ][ ][ ][ ][ ][ ]

APPLYING WHAT YOU KNOW

48. Steve's mother has a dominant gene for dark skin color. Steve's father has a dominant gene for light skin color. What color will Steve's skin most likely be?

49. Mr. and Mrs. Freund both carry recessive genes for cystic fibrosis. Using your knowledge of the Punnett square, estimate the probability of one of their offspring inheriting this condition.

50. Linda is pregnant and is over 40. She fears her age may predispose her baby to genetic disorders and she has sought the advice of a genetic counselor. What tests might the counselor suggest to alleviate Linda's fears?

51. Punnett Square

Fill in the Punnett square for the following genetic cases:

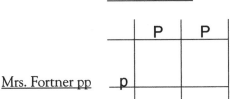

Mr. Fortner PP

Mrs. Fortner pp

Mr. Fortner has two dominant genes for brown eyes and Mrs. Fortner has two recessive genes for blue eyes.

a. The offspring of Mr. and Mrs. Fortner have a _____ % chance of having brown eyes and a _____ % chance of having blue eyes.
b. Will Mr. and Mrs. Fortner's offspring be carriers of blue eyes?
c. If Mr. and Mrs. Fortner's offspring mates with another offspring who is a carrier of blue eyes, what is the probability of the resulting offspring having blue eyes?

Draw your own Punnett square to determine your answer.

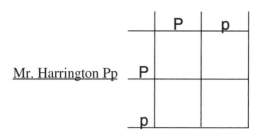

Mrs. Harrington Pp

Mr. and Mrs. Harrington are both carriers for albinism. Using the Punnett square, determine what percentage of Mr. and Mrs. Harrington's offspring will:

a.   Have normal pigmentation _____
b.   Be carriers _____
c.   Have albinism _____

52.   Word Find

Find and circle 14 terms presented in this chapter. Words may be spelled top to bottom, bottom to top, right to left, left to right, or diagonally.

```
N  J  A  T  E  T  O  G  Y  Z  S  F  I  H  Q
M  O  M  D  P  S  I  W  P  L  I  K  Y  E  K
S  M  N  P  E  E  F  Y  A  Z  S  A  X  M  C
F  A  I  D  V  M  M  Z  R  Z  O  R  P  O  L
H  R  O  J  I  O  E  U  E  I  I  Y  D  P  O
I  Q  C  M  S  S  O  L  H  Z  E  O  G  H  X
Y  J  E  O  S  O  J  Z  T  W  M  T  D  I  Q
G  E  N  I  E  M  C  U  E  I  E  Y  X  L  Q
A  O  T  G  C  O  P  K  N  E  J  P  I  I  G
M  P  E  M  E  R  D  A  E  C  P  E  J  A  I
E  D  S  I  R  H  N  C  G  B  T  Z  P  S  Y
T  G  I  D  U  C  G  C  P  X  H  I  F  G  X
E  W  S  R  E  I  R  R  A  C  V  I  O  H  S
S  W  V  B  K  R  C  R  Y  B  V  U  C  N  S
```

Amniocentesis	Gametes	Monosomy
Carrier	Gene therapy	Nondisjunction
Chromosomes	Hemophilia	Recessive
Codominance	Karyotype	Zygote
DNA	Meiosis	

DID YOU KNOW?

Scientists now believe the human body has 50,000 to 100,000 genes packed into just 46 chromosomes.

GENETICS

Fill in the crossword puzzle.

ACROSS

2. Name for the 22 pairs of matched chromosomes
3. Lack of melanin in the skin and eyes
6. Refers to genes that appear in the offspring
7. Chart that illustrates genetic relationships in a family over several generations
8. All genetic material in each cell
9. Scientific study of inheritance

DOWN

1. Trisomy 21 (two words)
4. Agents that cause genetic mutations
5. Triplet of autosomes rather than a pair
7. Excess of phenylketone in the urine (abbreviation)

CHECK YOUR KNOWLEDGE

Multiple Choice

Circle the correct answer.

1. Independent assortment of chromosomes ensures:
   A. Each offspring from a single set of parents is genetically unique
   B. At meiosis, each gamete receives the same number of chromosomes
   C. That the sex chromosomes always match
   D. An equal number of males and females are born

2. Which of the following statements is *not* true of a pedigree?
   A. They are useful to genetic counselors in predicting the possibility of producing offspring with genetic disorders.
   B. They may allow a person to determine his likelihood of developing a genetic disorder later in life.
   C. They indicate the occurrence of those family members affected by a trait, as well as carriers of the trait.
   D. All of the above are true of a pedigree.

3. The genes that cause albinism are:
   A. Codominant
   B. Dominant
   C. Recessive
   D. AA

4. During meiosis, matching pairs of chromosomes line up and exchange genes from their location to the same location on the other side; a process called:
   A. Gene linkage
   B. Crossing-over
   C. Cross-linkage
   D. Genetic variation

5. When a sperm cell unites with an ovum, a _____ is formed.
   A. Zygote
   B. Chromosome
   C. Gamete
   D. None of the above

6. DNA molecules can also be called:
   A. A chromatin strand
   B. A chromosome
   C. A and B
   D. None of the above

7. Nonsexual traits:
   A. Show up more often in females than in males
   B. May be carried on sex chromosomes
   C. Are the result of genetic mutation
   D. All of the above

8. If a person has only X chromosomes, that person is:
   A. Missing essential proteins
   B. Abnormal
   C. Female
   D. Male

9. A karyotype:
   A. Can detect trisomy
   B. Is useful for diagnosing a tubal pregnancy
   C. Is frequently used as a tool in gene augmentation therapy
   D. Can detect the presence of oncogenes

10. Which of the following pairs is mismatched?
    A. SCID—gene therapy
    B. Turner syndrome—trisomy
    C. PKU—recessive
    D. Cystic fibrosis—single-gene disease

Completion

Complete the following statements using the terms listed below. Write the corresponding letter in the answer blank.

A. Cystic fibrosis
B. Males
C. Phenylketonuria
D. Carrier
E. Genome
F. Females

G. Pedigree
H. Oncogenes
I. Karyotype
J. Tay-Sachs disease
K. Amniocentesis
L. Hemophilia

11. Abnormal genes called _____ are believed to be related to cancer.

12. Fetal tissue may be collected by a procedure called _____.

13. An abnormal accumulation of phenylalanine results in _____.

14. The entire collection of genetic material in each cell is called the _____.

15. _____ is caused by recessive genes in chromosome pair seven.

16. A _____ is a chart that illustrates genetic relationships over several generations.

17. A _____ is a person who has a recessive gene that is not expressed.

18. Absence of an essential lipid-producing enzyme may result in the recessive condition _____.

19. _____ is a recessive X-linked disorder.

20. Klinefelter syndrome occurs in _____.